Samuel Colt's Submarine Battery

THE SECRET AND THE ENIGMA

Philip K. Lundeberg

Smithsonian Institution Press
CITY OF WASHINGTON
1974

ABSTRACT

Lundeberg, Philip K. Samuel Colt's Submarine Battery: The Secret and the Enigma. *Smithsonian Studies in History and Technology*, number 29, 90 pages, 43 figures, 1974.—Samuel Colt's sustained efforts to secure the adoption of his Submarine Battery system as a major element in the coastal defenses of the United States have long constituted an obscure yet potentially significant episode in the technological development of undersea warfare. Stimulated not only by apparent threat of renewed British naval assaults on the Eastern seaboard early in the 1840s, but also by notable and well-publicized advances by British military engineers in galvanic underwater demolition techniques, the development of Colt's novel harbor defense system was supported by limited Congressional appropriations during 1841–44, as well as by the encouragement of Samuel F.B. Morse and John William Draper at the University of the City of New York. Colt secured no comparable assistance from the National Institute for the Promotion of Science, of which he was an early member.

The New England inventor's dogged secrecy regarding the precise character of his Submarine Battery, which he successfully maintained throughout four public demonstrations at Washington and New York, ultimately alienated cognizant military professionals, whose guidance or active participation Colt deliberately eschewed in refining his distinctive single and dual observer systems for mine firing control. Notwithstanding the apparent success of his climactic demonstration at the Washington Navy Yard in April 1844, the precise details of which yet remain open to conjecture, Colt was unable to secure War or Navy Department support either for the adoption of his galvanic mine system for coastal defense purposes or for Congressional payment of a contingent premium for the secret of his Submarine Battery.

OFFICIAL PUBLICATION DATE is handstamped in a limited number of initial copies and is recorded in the Institution's annual report, *Smithsonian Year*. SI PRESS NUMBER 5014. COVER DESIGN: "The Last Experiment of Mr. Colt's Submarine Battery in Washington City," 1844 by Aⁿ Gibert, reproduced by courtesy of Caldwell C. Robinson.

Library of Congress Cataloging in Publication Data
Lundeberg, Philip K.
Samuel Colt's Submarine Battery.
(Smithsonian studies in history and technology, no. 29)
Includes bibliographical references.
Supt. of Docs. no.: SI 1.28: 29
1. Mines, Submarine—History. 2. Colt, Samuel, 1814–1862. 3. United States—Coast
   defenses—History. I. Title. II. Series: Smithsonian Institution. Smithsonian studies in
   history and technology, no. 29.
V856.5.U6L86   623.4'5115   74–7322

Preface

The history of nineteenth-century military technology contains no more baffling chapter than the dogged and long-obscured efforts of the New England arms inventor, Samuel Colt, to secure the adoption of his Submarine Battery as a major element in the coastal defense system of the United States. Although the European and American antecedents of Colt's mine warfare system can be readily identified, the details of his own widely publicized yet curiously secretive demonstrations remain unclear. Virtually no connection has been established between his galvanic observation mine schemes and the remarkable development of mining operations witnessed during the American Civil War as part of the Confederate system of riverine and coastal defense. Friedrich von Ehrenkrook, in his pioneering survey, *Geschichte der Seeminen und Torpedos* (Berlin, 1878), was unable to establish a connection between the Yankee inventor's dual observer scheme, of which he was ignorant, and a similar system employed by the German inventor, Werner von Siemens, during the defense of Kiel in 1848, the first significant wartime employment of coastal minefields.

The obscurity surrounding the nature of Colt's Submarine Battery stemmed substantially from the almost obsessive secrecy with which that remarkable entrepreneur surrounded what was indeed the favorite creation of his early career. As his authorized biographer, Professor Henry Barnard, resignedly observed regarding Colt's galvanic mine scheme:

> In addition to this, Col. Colt claimed to possess a further secret, which many of his friends think died with him. But so reticent was he on the subject, that to this day it is not clear whether this secret related to the explosive compounds, or to the mode of arranging them, or to ascertaining at what instant it was necessary to fire the aquatic mine.*

As suggested by the subtitle of the present study, however, the secret of Colt's Submarine Battery—more specifically the practical details of the single and dual observer galvanic systems described in his long hidden patent application—has a less apparent yet equally intriguing counterpart in the enigmatic question of whether that inventor ever fully tested the purported elements of his novel system of undersea warfare. Owing to Colt's success in denying cognizant scientists and military specialists the opportunity to examine his plans and participate in his experiments, no substantive body of official evaluations were generated in his lifetime or indeed for a century thereafter. The report rendered to Congress in 1844 by Secretary of War William Wilkins, entitled *The Secret of Colt's Submarine Battery*, shed considerable light on the earlier evolution of galvanically controlled explosions, yet it contained virtually no data on any of that inventor's four governmentally funded demonstrations. Wilkins' report, substantial portions of which are reproduced in the Appendixes, affords a remarkable mirror of the frustration that befell government officials, scientific referees, and the stubborn inventor himself as the result of his obdurate secrecy.

For their generous assistance in helping me to grapple with the riddle of Samuel Colt's Submarine Battery, I should like to express my sincere appreciation to Mr.

---

*Henry Barnard, *Armsmear: The Home, the Arm, and the Armory of Samuel Colt: A Memorial* (New York: Alvord [printer], 1866), pages 287–288.

iii

Elmer Parker and his staff in the Old Military Records Branch of the U.S. National Archives; to Mr. Thompson R. Harlow, Director, and Mrs. Frances R. Hoxie of the Connecticut Historical Society; and to Mrs. Estella C. Lord, Director of the Connecticut State Library Museum. No student of Samuel Colt should neglect the penetrating insights into that doughty entrepreneur's extended encounter with the federal bureaucracy provided in William B. Edwards's sprightly account, *The Story of Colt's Revolver: The Biography of Col. Samuel Colt* (Harrisburg: Stackpole Co., 1953). I would, in addition, express my gratitude for challenging questions and valued insights offered by the former Chairman of the Mine Advisory Committee of the National Academy of Sciences, Professor Andrew Patterson, Jr., of the Sterling Chemistry Laboratory at Yale University; and to my sagacious colleague, Dr. Nathan Reingold, Editor of the Joseph Henry Papers in the Smithsonian Institution. Finally, for encouragement in seeking to shape one of the building blocks on which the history of technology is now emerging, I am deeply indebted to my friend and most generous colleague, Colonel Howard I. Chapelle, Historian Emeritus of the Smithsonian Institution. To these and numerous other helpful colleagues I am most grateful; they bear no responsibility for any errors that may appear herein.

Contents

The Advent of Galvanic Mine Warfare

...concerning the return to Col. Fitstum of 502 rubles, 72 kopecks, which he expended in the conduct of an experiment on underwater mines invented by him ..., Col. Fitstum himself wrote me about this matter and I replied that, considering all of the information which has been compiled on the matter, I was unable to find anything in his favor....

DIRECTOR OF THE MARINE MINISTRY TO THE
QUARTERMASTER SECTION, ST. PETERSBERG, 28 AUGUST 1810

The emergence of undersea warfare in the mid-nineteenth century has long been wrapped in an obscurity unusual even in the incompletely charted realm of military and naval technology. Several seminal episodes, notably including the attempts of David Bushnell to conduct mine and submarine warfare during the American Revolution, the extended experimentation of Robert Fulton with "torpedoes" and diving boats during the Napoleonic era, as well perhaps as the dogged efforts of Wilhelm Bauer to develop submersibles in the mid-nineteenth century, did indeed receive close scrutiny by early historians of undersea warfare.[1] Yet related technological developments, particularly those efforts by scientists, inventors, and entrepreneurs to apply newly discovered electrical phenomena to the destruction of shipping, have been relatively overlooked, save in Russia, where the first sustained program of research and development in sea mine warfare had been undertaken under the aegis of the Imperial Academy of Sciences during the decade and a half preceding the Crimean War.[2] In the present study, this writer has sought to probe the enigma of a particularly obscure American development, Samuel Colt's ill-starred Submarine Battery, whose nonfruition remains one of the most curiously anticlimatic episodes in the history of military technology in the United States.

The foundations of galvanic undersea warfare lie close to the mid-eighteenth century roots of electrical science. The technological kernel of the ensuing developments consisted of the detonation of gunpowder *under water* by means of electric current transmitted through insulated leads from a battery to an incandescent fuse lodged in the combustible charge. An early prefigurement was provided in 1751, when Benjamin Franklin of Philadelphia (Figure 1), then some five years launched into his investigations of "electric flame" and lightning, sounded out one of his frequent London correspondents, Peter Collinson of the Royal Academy, on 29 June:

I have not hear'd, that any of your European Electricians have heitherto been able to fire Gunpowder by the Electric Flame. We do it here in this Manner.

A small Cartridge is filled with Dry powder, hard rammed, so as to bruise some of the Grains. Two pointed Wires are then thrust In, one at Each End, the points approaching Each other in the Middle of the Cartridge, till within the distance of half an Inch: Then the Cartridge being placed in the Circle [circuit], when the Four Jarrs are discharged, the Electric Flame leaping from the point of one Wire to the point of the other, within the Cartridge, among the powder, fires It, and the Explosion of the powder is at the same Instant with the Crack of the Discharge.[3]

The Philadelphian's expansive scientific interests, revealed in 1751–54 with the publication of his *Experiments and Observations on Electricity, Made at Philadelphia* by Edward Cave in London, subsequently carried him on to more domestic applications, notably the lightning rod. Two decades later, as senior statesman of the American Revolution, Franklin had occasion to encourage several early protagonists of undersea warfare. On 22 July 1776, Franklin wrote

Philip K. Lundeberg, Division of Naval History, Department of National and Military History, National Museum of History and Technology, Smithsonian Institution, Washington, D.C. 20560.

Figure 1.—Benjamin Franklin, 1706–1790. Founder of the American Philosophical Society, this Boston-born printer first turned his restless imagination to the study of "electric fire" in 1746, the year that Pieter van Musschenbroek constructed the electric bottle later known as the Leyden jar. Franklin's subsequent correspondence with Peter Collinson regarding his electrical experiments at Philadelphia, culminating with his observations on the identity of lightning and electric current, led directly to his election to the Royal Society of London in 1756, as well as honorary degrees from Harvard, Yale, and William and Mary. When the Philadelphian reached London late in 1757 to represent the Pennsylvania Assembly's claims against that colony's proprietors, he was regarded throughout Europe as a leading natural philosopher of the age.

Figure 2.—"One of the kegs celebrated in the time of the Revolution." This keg mine was deposited with that attribution in 1793 in the Peale Museum of Philadelphia by Major George Fleming, formerly of the 2nd Continental Artillery. Fabricated at Bordentown, New Jersey, in the cooper shop of Colonel Joseph Borden and designed by an inventive pin maker, Joseph Plowman, these mines represented a community effort. The detonator element, consisting of a spring lock arrangement fabricated by gunsmith Robert Jackaway, was apparently triggered upon disturbance of a wooden firing arm by a passing vessel.

Measuring some 14½ inches in height and 13 inches in base diameter, Major Fleming's keg was fitted with a lid bearing the evident remnants of a wooden tripping arm which, connected to an iron pin, engaged a flintlock detonating device on the under side. Individual staves and supporting pieces of the wooden tripping arm are inscribed in sequence with roman numerals, a typical practice among colonial coopers and carpenters, suggesting further the mass-production of these venerable infernal devices.

The Fleming keg mine, secured by the Division of Naval History of The National Museum of History and Technology in 1972 from the Peabody Museum at Harvard University, had passed successively from the Peale Museum to the Boston Museum prior to reaching Cambridge. At present it is the oldest known example of a sea mine.

to General Washington, introducing Joseph Belton of Philadelphia, who had the previous fall proposed attacking British shipping by means of a semi-submersible "machine" capable of transporting a cannon to the vicinity of his targets. Belton may have assisted Captain John Hazelwood in his abortive fire-raft attack against the British frigates *Phoenix* and *Rose* near Tarrytown in August 1776.

No less dramatic events were soon to unfold on the Hudson. As early as August 1775, well before Belton's proposal, Franklin had received a letter from Benjamin Gale regarding a one-man submersible then being constructed in Connecticut by a young Yale student,

David Bushnell, for attacks on British shipping. En route to Boston in October, Franklin's interest in underwater demolition was aroused when he visited Bushnell's secret workshop near Saybrook. There he examined the young inventor's system of limpet mine warfare, utilizing a hand-propelled, one-man submersible, the *Turtle*, which was destined to conduct its historic if unsuccessful attack on Vice Admiral Richard Lord Howe's flagship *Eagle* at New York on 7 September 1776, the high point of American underwater operations on the Hudson.[4]

Evidence is lacking that the earlier galvanic detonations conducted by Franklin (who departed for France in the fall of 1776) influenced either Bushnell's subsequent ventures with the *Turtle* at New York or his unsuccessful effort of 5 January 1778, in collaboration with New Jersey patriots, to attack British naval units on the Delaware with a score of floating contact mines.[5] The oaken-staved contact mine (Figures 2 and 3) may well be the type employed by Bushnell on this occasion.

That abortive if amusing episode in Philadephia's maritime history, celebrated in Francis Hopkinson's mock-heroic ballad, "The Battle of the Kegs," marked the obscure beginnings of modern naval mine warfare (Figures 2 and 3), but its relevance to an account of galvanic undersea warfare development lies in its rough chronological proximity to early European investigations into the electrical detonation of gunpowder. Stimulated by the publications of Franklin, Priestley, and Beccaria, as well as by early experimentation in telegraphy, those investigations proved particularly attractive in Italy. In May 1777 Alessandro Volta, then Professor of Physics in the Royal School at Como and destined to provide in his electric "pile" the first source of continuous electrical current, wrote to Marchese Francesco Castelli, briefly describing experiments in which he had fired pistols, muskets, and finally a submarine mine (*mine subacquee*) by means of a bulbous eudiometrical device that triggered combustible gases serving as the detonating agent.[6] A different approach was followed by Volta's friend, Tiberius Cavallo, who as early as 1782 undertook to detonate gunpowder by electric current passed through what appears to have been a precursor of the incandescent filament. Cavallo, who had been admitted to the Royal Society of London in 1779, provided an arresting description of his more extensive subsequent experiments, evidently inspired by early ventures in telegraphy, in the fourth edition of his *Complete Treatise on Electricity*, published at London in 1795:

The attempts recently made to convey intelligence from one place to another at a great distance, with the utmost quickness, have induced me to publish the following experiments, which I made some years ago....

Figure 3.—FLINTLOCK DETONATOR FOR REVOLUTIONARY WAR CONTACT MINE. An important element of Major Fleming's keg mine is a remaining portion of the lock plate of a Brown Bess flintlock musket, marked with the British crown (no Royal cypher indicated) and the name of "Galton" (the Galton family which manufactured flintlock firearms at Birmingham and London during the period 1750–1813). This lock plate fits into recesses in two wooden supports on the under side of the keg's cover. Evidently missing from this firing device are connecting elements, possibly including springs, between the lock plate and the curved hook of an iron pin connected with the iron and wooden firing arm on the keg cover's top. This particular keg mine may be an incomplete prototype, as there is no evidence that pitch or other waterproofing had been applied to it.

The object for which those experiments were performed, was to fire gun-powder, or other combustible matter, from a great distance, by means of electricity. At first I made a circuit with a very long brass wire, the two ends of which returned to the same place, whilst the middle of the wire stood at a great distance. In this middle an interruption was made, in which a cartridge of gun-powder mixed with steel filings was placed. Then, by applying a charged Leyden phial to the two extremities of the wire, (viz. by touching one wire with the knob of the phial, whilst the other was connected with the outside coating) the cartridge was fired. In this manner I could fire gun-powder from the distance of three hundred feet and upwards.[7]

Cavallo, whose *Treatise on Magnetism in Theory and Practice* (1787) summed up existing scientific knowledge in that field, encountered problems with bare wire leads and incandescent materials suitable for his fuses that were to preoccupy his successors in undersea warfare development for over half a century.[8] Like Cavallo, those Continental successors came upon the application of galvanism to mine warfare somewhat incident to their pioneering research in the transmission of information by electricity. Of particular transitional importance was the work of the Prussian anatomist Samuel Thomas Sömmerring (1755–1830), a graduate of the University of Göttingen whose studies had led him as early as 1778 to Holland, England, and Scotland. Sömmerring, whose subsequent work was influenced by the galvano-chemical research of Humphry Davy, devised in the summer of 1809 a small galvanic telegraph apparatus which he demonstrated on 29 August to the Bavarian Academy of Sciences at Munich. Although unsuccessful in his efforts to interest Napoleon Bonaparte in military applications of this device—the French had but recently introduced their optical telegraph system—Sömmerring in 1810 attracted the attention of Baron Pavel L'vovich Schilling von Canstadt (Figure 4), a member of the Russian diplomatic mission to the Bavarian capital who had strong scientific interests. Impressed by a simple telegraphic alarm devised by Sömmerring, Baron Schilling introduced the physicist to Russian and Bavarian military engineers and subsequently collaborated with him in several telegraphic experiments. Encouraged by visits from diplomats and other government officials, as well as from the renowned Baron Alexander von Humboldt, Sömmerring continued his experiments with wire insulated with India rubber and varnish, succeeding in March 1812 in telegraphing through some 10,000 feet of cable.[9]

The approach of hostilities between Russia and France in the spring of 1812 intensified Baron Schilling's preoccupation with the insulated conduction of electric current under water and through long distances, not only to transmit military dispatches but also to detonate mines planted on the opposite bank of a defended river from a controlling observer. Upon his recall to St. Petersburg in July, this Baltic nobleman further developed his evolving mine warfare system, insulating the cables with tarred hemp and copper tubing and devising a carbon-arc fuse, consisting of two charged pieces of pointed charcoal, which proved remarkably reliable.[10] In the fall of 1812, the Baron carried out a successful, if scantily documented, mining demonstration near the tsarist capital, detonating powder charges that were controlled from the opposite bank of the Neva River. Although Russian military engineers do not appear

Figure 4.—BARON PAVEL L'VOVICH SCHILLING VON CANSTADT, 1786–1837. This talented Balt, born at Reval in 1786, began his military education in the Imperial cadet corps in 1797. Upon commissioning in 1802 at the age of sixteen, the precocious Schilling was posted to the General Staff of the Russian army, subsequently serving from 1803–1812 as military attaché in the Russian embassy at Munich. His experiments with galvanically detonated mines, though not presently well documented, establish him as an important pioneer of defensive mine warfare.

to have adopted his galvanic system at that critical juncture in the Napoleonic invasion, Baron Schilling retained a lively interest in its development. Joining a regiment of hussars in 1813, he subsequently participated in the allied invasion of France, entering Paris in the spring of 1814 with the army of Alexander I. As recalled by his first biographer, Joseph Hamel of the Russian Imperial Academy of Sciences, "Baron Schilling has told me that during his stay in Paris he, with his subaqueous conductor several times, to the astonishment of the lookers-on, ignited gunpowder across the river Seine." [11]

While Sömmerring's subsequent research dealt increasingly with development of the voltaic pile, Baron Schilling continued his mining experiments, on several occasions demonstrating the action of his carbon-arc igniters to Alexander I at the tsar's summer camp near St. Petersburg. As Hamel reported, in the diffident vernacular of the court:

> Once Baron Schilling had the honor to present a wire to the Emperor in his tent. He begged his Majesty to touch it with another wire, whilst looking through the door of the tent in the direction of a very far distant mine. A cloud of smoke rose from this exploding mine at the moment the Emperor, with his hands, made the contact. This caused great surprise, and provoked expressions of satisfaction and applause.[12]

Although increasingly preoccupied with his postwar duties as director of the tsarist regime's first lithographic establishment, Baron Schilling found time to invent the first electromagnetic telegraph, utilizing in his system the galvanometer multiplier of Johann Schweigger, Sömmerring's alarm, and from one to five needles. The Baron, invested in 1818 as a Knight of the Order of St. Anne, demonstrated his magnetic telegraph at St. Petersburg repeatedly, later exhibiting it on journeys to Mongolia and in 1835 to Western Europe. Evidence is presently lacking as to whether Schilling's ideas on mine warfare were influenced by earlier experiments, conducted by Lieutenant Colonel Ivan I. Fitstum of the Russian Army Engineer Corps, that had been intended to perfect a system of fireships and underwater coast defense mines which could be fired by conventional artillery fuses. Colonel Fitstum, whose difficulties with sodden fuses had led him to propose galvanic ignition, had suffered the misfortune of having his project and indeed his considerable experimentation costs summarily rejected in 1810 by an unsympathetic Marine Ministry in St. Petersburg. Shortly after Schilling's death in 1837, the Baron's pioneering efforts in galvanic mine development were reviewed at the Imperial Academy of Sciences by a young Prussian émigré, Moritz Hermann von Jacobi, who two years later was appointed by Nicholas I as scientific leader of a joint services Committee on Underwater Experiments, a working group destined to carry through a sustained program of galvanic mine development during the fifteen years prior to the onset of the Crimean War.[13]

The vital importance of sustained institutional support for such developments in military technology was to be strikingly demonstrated both in Europe and the United States during the half decade from 1839 to 1844. While Professor Jacobi and a small corps of *sapeurs galvaniques* experimented with increasingly sophisticated prototypes of observation and contact mines at St. Petersburg, the Corps of Royal Sappers and Miners of the British Army, operating from

Figure 5.—COLONEL COMMANDANT CHARLES WILLIAM PASLEY, 1780–1861. A notable figure in the development of British military engineering, Pasley was born at Dumfries, Scotland, and entered the Royal Military Academy at Woolwich in 1796. Following commissioning in the Corps of Royal Engineers in 1799, he served in the Mediterranean and in 1807 took part in the siege of Copenhagen. After service in the Peninsular Campaign under Sir John Moore, Captain Pasley participated in the Walcheren Expedition and was severely wounded at the siege of Flushing in 1809.

During his recovery, Pasley wrote and published the first edition of his influential *Essay on the Military Policy and Institutions of the British Empire* (1810), a trenchant appeal for greater energy in accomplishing the downfall of Napoleon. Major Pasley was supported by the Duke of Wellington in his advocacy of more thoroughly professional training of British military engineers and in 1812 was appointed Director of the Royal Engineer's Institution for Field Instruction at Chatham. As Colonel Commandant of the Corps of Royal Sappers and Miners, he steadily enlarged the program of instruction, contributing himself numerous professional publications including his classic *Practical Operations of a Siege* (1829). A member of the Royal Society since 1816, Pasley was an early advocate of the decimal system in England, was appointed Inspector General of Railways in 1841, and three years later received an honorary doctorate from Oxford.

Figure 6.—SIR CHARLES WHEATSTONE, 1802–1875.   A principal developer of the practical telegraph, Wheatstone was one of a notable series of European scientists whose contributions to the development of telegraphy were applied to the galvanic detonation of explosives under water. Following publication of his study on harmonic motion in the *Transactions* of the Royal Society of London in 1833, he made pioneering contributions to the study of optics and light, including the principle of the stereoscope and of the prismatic analysis of electric light.

Shortly after assuming the Professorship of Experimental Philosophy at King's College, London, in 1834, Wheatstone undertook extensive experiments on the rate of transmission of electricity through copper wire. In association with William Fothergill Cooke, he subsequently investigated the transmission of messages by electricity and developed the five-needle telegraph. Wheatstone was knighted in 1868 and at his death bequeathed his instruments and library to King's College, where they are preserved in the Wheatstone Laboratory.

Chatham under Colonel Commandant Charles William Pasley (Figure 5), had in August 1839 under-

taken the removal of the wreck of the 100-gun ship-of-the-line *Royal George*, which had sunk off Portsmouth in 1782. Colonel Pasley, who recognized in this difficult salvage operation an excellent training exercise for his Corps, had earlier directed the removal of two sunken merchantmen, the *William* and the *Glenmorgan*, from the Gravesend Reach on the Thames, demolishing them with large submerged charges fired by artillery fuses.[14] The idea of employing electricity to detonate these waterproofed charges first struck Pasley in reading London newspaper accounts of an ordnance accident that had occurred near St. Petersburg in the fall of 1837, when Tsar Nicholas I had narrowly escaped death from fragments of a bridge demolished by a mine fired by voltaic battery. Colonel Pasley thereupon sought the advice of Charles Wheatstone (Figure 6), Michael Faraday, and John Frederic Daniell, three of Britain's most distinguished galvanic scientists, regarding the feasibility of firing submerged charges by means of electricity. Wheatstone, a fellow member of the Royal Society, had carried out numerous experiments on the conduction of electricity through copper wire and had developed a five-needle telegraph in collaboration with William Fothergill Cooke. At Wheatstone's suggestion, Pasley employed Daniell's new voltaic cell as his power source.[15] The ensuing removal of the *Royal George*, which engaged the Chatham engineers for six instructive working seasons, proved a milestone in the development of modern marine salvage and witnessed the successful employment of August Siebe's closed diving suit with its copper helmet and weighted shoes. Colonel Pasley's galvanic equipment, which included insulated copper cables and platinum filament detonators, received international attention in scientific and military journals of the day, stimulating renewed interest in both Russia and the United States in serious efforts to apply the growing elements of galvanic technology to undersea mine warfare.[16] Meanwhile British military engineers had experimented both in India and Bermuda with further applications of electrical demolition systems to marine salvage operations.[17]

The Genesis of Colt's Submarine Battery

*My experiment in the Medway was with a very small charge only, as I do not
choose to invite spectators to an exhibition with any chance of failure.*

COLONEL CHARLES WILLIAM PASLEY, R. E., to
MICHAEL FARADAY, CHATHAM, 9 FEBRUARY 1839

Early contributions to the technology of undersea warfare offered by private entrepreneurs, normally conceived outside of military establishments, often met undisguised official hostility. The difficulties encountered by Robert Fulton in seeking government support in France, Great Britain, and the United States for sustained development of his torpedo warfare systems (Figure 7) stemmed from both frank skepticism and genuine apprehension among experienced naval officers, who recognized therein an ultimate threat to their squadrons of wooden-walled warships, the traditional basis of sea power.[18] Fulton was not the last American inventor to be confounded by professional criticism and the absence of national institutions prepared to nurture such unusual and patently commercial enterprises.

Some three decades later another enterprising Yankee, Samuel Colt of Hartford, (Figure 8) found himself similarly frustrated in his efforts to secure government adoption of his novel system of galvanic mine warfare, at that juncture by both established scientists and military engineers. The latter were currently committed to the completion of a comprehensive national program of coastal fortifications, erected upon the ruins of more haphazardly conceived Colonial and post-Revolutionary systems. Develop-

ment of that Third System had received strong Congressional support following the War of 1812, which had witnessed the burning of the nation's weakly defended capital. This Third System of coastal fortifications had been projected as the central element of that comprehensive national defense establishment proposed in 1821 by a military board headed by Brigadier General Simon Bernard, USA, an experienced French military engineer who had emigrated to the United States following extensive service under Napoleon on the Continent.[19]

Figure 7.—DESTRUCTION OF THE BRIG *Dorothea* OFF WALMER, ENGLAND, ON 15 OCTOBER 1805 BY A "TORPEDO". This plate from Robert Fulton's treatise on *Torpedo Warfare* (1810) strikingly indicates the model for Samuel Colt's dramatic demonstrations of his Submarine Battery at New York and Washington in 1842 and 1844. This and other illustrations from Fulton's pamphlet were reproduced in 1834 in the first volume of the *American State Papers: Naval Affairs,* to which Colt specifically referred in his letter to President John Tyler on 19 June 1841.

Figure 8.—SAMUEL COLT, 1814–1862. A notable entrepreneur of mid-nineteenth century New England, Colt was the son of a Hartford textile manufacturer who suffered severe reverses during the Panic of 1819. Following apprenticeship in his father's dyeing establishment at Ware, Massachusetts, young Sam attended Amherst Academy before going to sea in 1830. Returning from India with a wooden model of his celebrated revolver, he forwarded its preliminary description to the Patent Office in 1832. Four years later, after securing patents in England and France, Colt obtained his first American patent, and at the age of twenty-two became a partner in the Patent Arms Manufacturing Company of Paterson, New Jersey.

Substantial government arms contracts eluded Colt, owing to unfavorable proving-ground reports, and in 1842 the Paterson firm collapsed. During the ensuing half decade, the young inventor turned his attention to submarine telegraphy, providing assistance—principally in the development of insulated electrical cable—to Samuel F.B. Morse during his historic experiments at New York and Washington. In addition to making this pioneering contribution, Colt sought governmental adoption of his tinfoil cartridges and of his long-obscure "Submarine Battery." At the outset of the Mexican War, Colt undertook production of an improved revolver, initially at Whitneyville, near New Haven, and from 1847 at Hartford, where he established a world-renowned armory, whose efficient management, machine tool equipment and enlightened employee relations made it a notable model of mid-nineteenth century American enterprise.

Architectually characterized by the employment of massive casemated fortifications situated to command the approaches to selected naval anchorages and important shipping entrepôts, the Third System was already well advanced by 1829, when the inventive Colt, then a lad of fourteen, first investigated the possibilities of firing explosive charges *under water* as the basis for what he later and most imprudently was to advocate as a more economical system of coastal defense. As Colt ultimately affirmed to Congress in an account of the development of his system of mine warfare:

> The idea of Submarine explosions for the purposes of Harbour defence was conceived by me as early as the year 1829 while stud[y]ing in the laboratory of a bleeching and colouring establishment at Ware Vilage Massachusetts, and I made sundry experiments on a small scale at that time and repeated them in various ways for several successive years thereafter.[20]

Although based on the recollections of Colt's earliest professional associate, the noted New England mechanic Elisha K. Root, precise information on the youthful inventor's "sundry experiments" is lacking. Evidently on the basis of close study of a popular compendium of knowledge that contained articles on galvanic batteries and the formulation of gunpowder, Sam Colt tried a hand at developing explosive compounds by testing various mixtures of charcoal, nitre, and sulphur, a hazardous venture not dissimilar to Immanuel Nobel's risky early experiments at Stockholm. Colt's gunpowder trials, by no means unusual in themselves, led him to consider the problem of detonating explosives *under water*, which he initially solved by means of galvanic current communicated from a simple battery (or possibly a Leyden jar) through a tarred copper wire. His initial demonstration at Ware Pond, long remembered in that neighborhood, was attempted on the Fourth of July 1829, as Root recalled years later:

> It had been noised around that a youngster—one Sam. Colt—would blow up a raft on the pond that day, and so I with other apprentices of the neighborhood walked some way to see the sight. An explosion was produced, but the raft was by no means blown sky-high. Yet, curious regarding the boy's explosive contrivances, I then and there made his acquaintance.[21]

The irate villagers, thoroughly drenched as Colt's crude device erupted *near* rather than *under* the raft, failed to share Root's dim awareness that a significant technical feat had been achieved. Stung by the jibes of his onlookers, Colt derived from this youthful venture a burning appreciation of the importance of accurate target location, a feature notably characteristic of his later mine warfare proposals. Although increasingly involved thereafter in fashioning the revolving-cylinder firearm that he patented in 1836, this budding Yankee entrepreneur retained a strong theatrical flair—supporting his early arms experimentation by touring the Eastern seaboard as the celebrated "Dr. Coult," demonstrating the amusing effects of nitrous oxide or "laughing gas"—as well as a lively interest in ultimately creating a galvanic system capable of detonating submerged charges *with precision*, in the immediate vicinity of selected moving target vessels. [22]

Samuel Colt's notion of employing electric current to fire explosive or flammable substances was by no means unique, even in the United States—a fact that was to loom large in the ultimate frustration of his matured mine warfare proposals. As early as 1820, Robert Hare (Figure 9), recently appointed Professor of Chemistry at the University of Pennsylvania, had described in Benjamin Silliman's *American Journal of Science and Arts* a method of igniting flammable gases contained in a eudiometrical apparatus (Figure 10) by means of a "calorimotor," a galvanic battery of the plunge type (Figure 11) that he had devised containing twenty-two alternate plates of zinc and copper (Figure 12).[23] Although the Philadelphian's original purpose with this arrangement had been to analyze various gaseous mixtures, he subsequently became interested in applying electric current more practically to the hazardous business of rock blasting, then the cause of numerous fatal accidents. In 1831 Professor Hare received a request from Moses Shaw, a New York inventor and entrepreneur, for assistance in devising a safer method of blasting by means of galvanic current discharged from a Leyden jar. This cumbersome method of providing an igniting spark to fulminating powder poured into rock crevasses had proven unsatisfactory in wet weather, leading Hare to propose a firing system employing his calorimotor:

It occurred to me, as soon as this statement was made by Mr. Shaw, that the ignition of gunpowder, for the purpose he had in view, might be effected by a galvanic discharge from a deflagrator, or calorimotor, in a mode which I have long used in my eudiometrical experiments to ignite explosive gaseous mixtures. This process is free from the uncertainty, which is always more or less attendant upon the employment of mechanical electricity, for similar purposes.[24]

Figure 9.—ROBERT HARE, 1781–1858. The son of a successful Philadelphia brewer, Hare learned the scientific method as a student of James Woodhouse at the University of Pennsylvania. His inventive bent became apparent as early as 1801, when he described to the Chemical Society of Philadelphia his oxyhydrogen blowpipe, a device that generated intense heat for experimental purposes. Elected to the American Philosophical Society in 1803, Hare was awarded the degree of Doctor of Medicine by Yale University three years later and was, in 1818, appointed Professor of Chemistry at the University of Pennsylvania. A pioneer of physical chemistry, Hare, in 1827, published his *Compendium of Chemistry*, the first substantially illustrated American text on chemistry, which significantly influenced the subsequent works of his friend Benjamin Silliman of Yale. Hare's invention of the calorimotor in 1819 reflected this early American chemist's preoccupation with electrical phenomena. As his biographer observed, "Caloric, light and electricity were the agents to which Hare was constantly exposing chemical substances." In addition to some 150 papers for Silliman's *American Journal of Science and Arts*, Hare published extended essays on "The Origin and Progress of Galvanism, or Voltaic Electricity" and "On Electro-Magnetism," which were incorporated in the fourth edition of the *Compendium of Chemistry* (1840), which appeared on the eve of his fruitful trans-Atlantic correspondence with Michael Faraday.

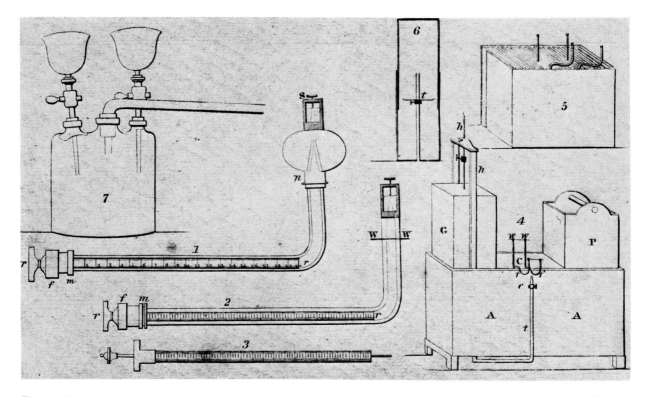

Figure 10.—ROBERT HARE'S EUDIOMETRICAL APPARATUS. Two early types of calibrated glass-tube eudiometers (see sketches 1 and 2) designed to introduce measured quantities of flammable gas into a glass combustion bulb (n) that was fitted with an incandescent wire. Current to heat this filament was generated by a plunge-type battery or calorimotor (sketch 5), which was fitted in a cistern (AA in sketch 4), being located adjacent (beneath C) to the gasometer (G).

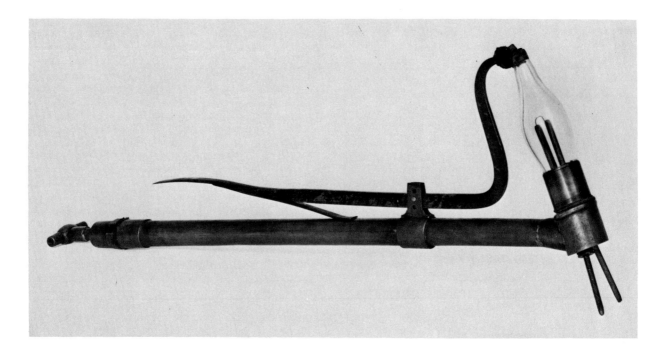

Following extensive experimentation, during which he constructed a plunge-type "galvanic machine" that contained sixteen zinc and twenty copper plates, Hare reported in 1833 in the *Journal of the Franklin Institute*:

I have ignited as many as twelve charges of gunpowder at the distance of one hundred and thirty feet, from the galvanic machine employed. This distance is much greater than is necessary to the safety of the operator, as the deflagrator may be shielded so as not to be injured by the explosion, and by means of levers and pulleys it may be made to act at any distance which may be preferred.[25]

Scarcely less important than the galvanic machine incorporated in Hare's rock blasting system was a tubular firing device that he fashioned for detonating individual charges sealed in selected crevasses or drill holes. Consisting of a cylinder of tinned iron fitted with ignition wire and a wooden plug packed with fulminating powder, this simple galvanic fuse suggested additional applications to Hare, who observed: "It must be obvious that in all cases of blasting under water, the plan of a tin tube, and ignition by a galvanic circuit, must be very eligible." [26] In concluding his remarkable essay on the employment of galvanic current for rock blasting, this pioneer of American experimental chemistry foresaw practical military applications as well:

It can scarcely be necessary to point out that the method of communicating ignition described here for the purpose of rock-blasting, may be applied as the means of exploding a mine. As, for instance, the mines associated with the fortifications erecting near Newport, as a part of the means of annoyance, might have a communication through copper wires, with a galvanic apparatus, in those situations to which the besieged might be expected to retire; putting it thus completely in the power of the commanding officer to select the time for the explosion when its effects would be most serviceable.[27]

Hare appears to have been misinformed regarding the Army's intentions of employing sea or land mines at Newport, Rhode Island, during the thirties. Work had steadily progressed there since 1824 on the construction of massively casemated Fort Adams, but

Figure 11.—HARE'S "AQUEOUS, SLIDING-ROD, HYDRO-OXYGEN EUDIOMETER" (replica). Reconstructed on the basis of fragmentary original portions of Hare's eudiometer in the Robert Hare Collection, Division of Physical Sciences, The National Museum of History and Technology, Smithsonian Institution. This instrument included a copper filament connecting the poles within the glass combustion chamber.

Figure 12.—ROBERT HARE'S CALORIMOTOR. This plunge-type galvanic battery, part of a collection deposited by Hare in the nascent Smithsonian Institution in 1847 following his retirement, was among the earliest specimens of "philosophical apparatus" secured by Joseph Henry for that national institution. Substantially similar to the calorimotor that Hare had described in the *American Journal of Science and Arts* in 1819, this galvanic device was notable in that all copper plates were connected and all zinc plates were similarly connected, thus in effect creating one large pair of electrodes, "instead of multiplying the pairs of galvanic plates." Like earlier plunge-type batteries devised by William Pepys, C.H. Wilkinson, and Humphry Davy in England, Hare's calorimotor had the advantage of limiting corrosion of the plates to the period of actual immersion in the electrolyte. Its subsequent employment by Hare for rock blasting during 1831–33 received substantial attention in American scientific circles.

official correspondence of the Corps of Engineers and surviving plans of those works reveal no provision for minefields, with or without galvanic control. The letterbooks of Colonel Joseph G. Totten, U.S. Engineers, who had his headquarters at Fort Adams for more than a decade while supervising the construction of fortifications in New England and on the Northern Lakes, contain no allusion to utilizing mines at any of those sites as auxiliary means of defense. It may be noted, however, that on 15 May 1832, Colonel Totten had written to Major General Joseph G. Swift, former Chief of the Corps of Engineers, regarding rock blasting that had been conducted at Newport during the construction of Fort Adams. After describing safety procedures and the use of steel drills and blasting cartridges, Totten observed that "the electrical spark may be useful in obtaining very long blocks of stone, either to be used in mass or to be regularly split up for building stones—but will never, I think, be substituted for the present mode in common operations. . . ." [28] That the requisite technology for introducing a system of sea mines was present at Newport is obvious; but evidence of an intent to employ such auxiliary ordnance is clearly lacking.

Robert Hare's conception during 1833 of utilizing sea mines *in conjunction with coastal fortifications* nevertheless proved strikingly prophetic of those complex coastal defense systems that evolved in Europe and the United States during the latter half of the nineteenth century, largely under the control, it should be emphasized, of military engineers of the respective nations. That the United States did not, as in the case of Russia, integrate observation mines with its Third System of coastal fortifications during the two decades prior to the Civil War appears to stem in no small part from the fact that Samuel Colt, as principal American proponent of galvanic harbor mines in that era, represented their utility in a manner that antagonized those military officials charged with long-range development of the nation's system of coastal fortifications, a system then approaching the climax of its technical development.

For the remainder of the thirties, the fledgling Yankee entrepreneur found himself heavily engaged in promoting the manufacture and sale of his remarkable revolver and similarly designed repeating rifles. Following incorporation of the Patent Arms Manufacturing Company at Paterson. New Jersey, in 1836, Colt repeatedly visited Washington in high hope of securing substantial contracts from the War and Navy

Departments. His Congressional lobbying efforts, which established Colt's reputation in the capital as an unstinting host, nevertheless met with studied official reserve. Limited numbers of Paterson-built revolvers and carbines were purchased by the embattled Republic of Texas toward the close of the decade, but orders from the United States Army proved so disappointing, following unfavorable evaluation of Colt's weapons by the Ordnance Board, that the Patent Arms establishment collapsed early in 1842. By that juncture, Colt was also directing his restless energies to the development of waterproof tinfoil cartridges—a venture which convinced the inventor that he had little prospect of receiving effective cooperation from the Ordnance Board—and submarine mines, the latter destined to lead him briefly into the field of commercial telegraphy, in collaboration with Samuel F. B. Morse. [29]

Samuel Colt's renewed involvement in the development of mine warfare materiel was by no means attributable to the failure of the Paterson venture. As early as 1836, during a period of deteriorating Franco-American relations, the 21-year-old inventor's imagination had been roused by President Andrew Jackson's vigorous measures to strengthen the nation's naval establishment and coastal defenses. During July, while yet engaged in setting up revolver production at Paterson, Colt had sketched a scheme for tracking the movements of a man-of-war through a river minefield by means of visual cross-bearings coordinated by two shore observers (Figure 13). Although undocumented, aside from the notation "Paterson 4 July 1836," this simple conceptual drawing indicates Colt's renewed preoccupation with the problem, embarrassingly revealed in his Ware Pond experiment, of detonating observation mines only when the target vessel was in their immediate vicinity. It was in this pioneering consideration of methods of accurate minefield surveillance that Colt was to make his greatest, albeit virtually unknown, contribution to the evolution of modern undersea warfare. As would later become apparent, Colt's initial two-observer conception foreshadowed the observation mine system devised for the defense of Kiel harbor on the Western Baltic in 1848 by Werner von Siemens, a scientifically talented young Prussian artillerist (Figure 14). [30]

Colt's imagination soon carried him beyond this classic two-observer scheme, however, for in 1836 he also draughted some "first thorts" on his celebrated and secrecy-enshrouded "Submarine Batary," a

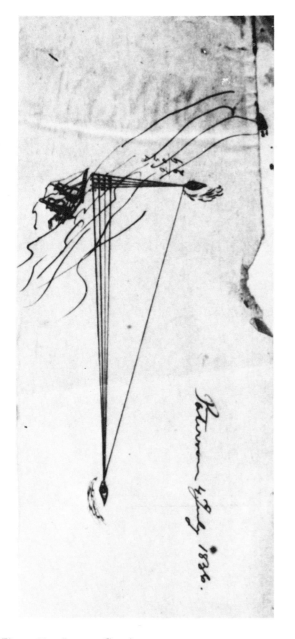

Figure 14.—WERNER VON SIEMENS, 1819–1892. Born near Hanover, this notable German inventor joined the Prussian Army in 1838, following graduation from the Royal Artillery and Engineer School in Berlin. During early duty as an artillerist, he exhibited strong proclivities for scientific experimentation with explosives.

By the mid-forties, European governments had become actively interested in the success of Charles Wheatstone and William F. Cooke in demonstrating the feasibility of commercial and, by implication, military telegraphy. In 1846, von Siemens was appointed to a Royal Commission created to establish an underground telegraph system in Prussia. Through the suggestion of his elder brother Wilhelm, he became aware of the insulating properties of gutta percha, and in 1847 he directed the successful completion of an experimental telegraph line in the Berlin suburbs.

During the ensuing Schleswig-Holstein War in 1848, von Siemens collaborated with his brother-in-law, Professor Karl Himly of the University of Kiel, in designing and laying a field of galvanically controlled mines in the approaches to Kiel that effectively discouraged Danish naval bombardment of that seaport. Following these early achievements, von Siemens emerged rapidly as an international entrepreneur of telegraphic systems, completing numerous major lines in both Prussia and Russia and ultimately attaining stature as a giant of early German scientific industry.

Figure 13.—SAMUEL COLT'S INITIAL CONCEPTION OF A TWO-OBSERVER MINEFIELD, DRAWN AT PATERSON, NEW JERSEY, 4 JULY 1836. This two-observer system for controlling a river minefield involved the employment of prearranged multiple sighting lines laid to intersect at the location of individual mine cases. What solution Colt envisaged for communication between the observers is not evident either in this sketch or in his patent application for the Submarine Battery in 1844, which cited [see Appendix 12] the two-observer system as an alternate means of achieving accurate control of the detonations. He appears to have contemplated a field of 16 to 29 mines, perhaps with the Passaic River, flowing past the Paterson factory, as the basis of his conception.

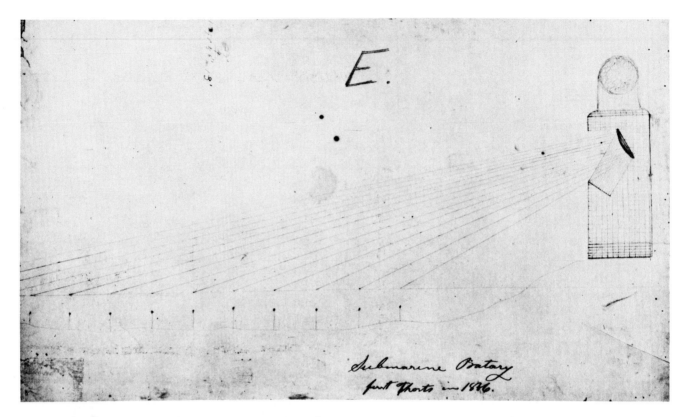

Figure 15.—SAMUEL COLT'S "SUBMARINE BATARY" CON-
CEPTION, 1836. These "first thorts" include no visible
indication of a galvanic element. Clearly evident is Colt's
scheme for reflecting the image of his minefield, possibly
buoyed as in later German practice, onto a control panel
located in a "torpedo tower" overlooking the field.

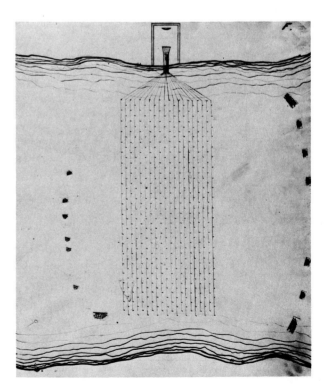

Figure 16.—OVERHEAD VIEW OF COLT'S SUBMARINE BAT-
TERY (undated).   Decorated with woodblock prints of merchantmen (cut from commercial journals), this overhead
perspective of Colt's "torpedo tower" and adjacent river
minefield clearly reveals the inventor's conception of a control panel studded with numerous metallic terminals connecting with individual mines. Located behind the control
panel is an apparently globular mirror, mounted overhead to
reflect an image of the entire field on the panel.

remarkably original single-observer system (Figure 15) for precise visual control of extensive minefields, which he began cautiously promoting early in the forties. The most salient element of this novel conception was an enclosed "torpedo tower," a galvanic firing post very possibly of masonry construction. Within this shore observation post would be installed a ten-foot convex mirror, positioned above and behind the galvanic operator in order to reflect the image of an adjacent minefield onto the mirrored control grid before him.[31] Embedded in this control panel, as suggested in Colt's later overhead perspective of the observation post and nearby river minefield, were envisaged numerous individual metallic terminals from several score anchored mines, each terminal being located upon the control grid's equivalent of its mine's watery position (Figure 16). As ultimately envisaged by Colt, his observer-operative, seated before the galvanic control panel (Figures 41 and 42), would be capable of triggering selected clusters of mines as a target ship's image moved across the minefield grid, by completing appropriate circuits with a lead from a battery located beneath the control panel. Central to the development of this conception was the inventor's determination to achieve accurate target location, a problem which European submarine ordnance specialists had not yet addressed. Inherent in Colt's single- and two-observer schemes however, was the weakness —those systems' ineffectiveness in darkness or fog— that would ultimately necessitate the incorporation of contact detonators in effective observation mine systems.[32]

The Approach to the Congress

The result of this course of experiments [at Chatham] *may be of great importance, especially for defensive military mines, because the Voltaic battery affords the only possible means of firing several such mines, not only instantly but simultaneously . . . .*

Army and Navy Chronicle, WASHINGTON, 13 JUNE 1839

Deteriorating Anglo-American relations early in 1841, arising principally from the Maine boundary dispute, finally projected Samuel Colt into active advocacy of his novel system of coastal defense. Well aware of several rival schemes that emerged for Congressional consideration at this juncture, including Uriah Brown's fireship and John Webster

Cochran's "multi-chambered bomb cannon," Colt had also been closely following the accounts of those galvanic demolitions conducted by the Royal Sappers and Miners during the salvage of the *Royal George*, published in the *Army and Navy Chronicle* (Figure 17).[33] Being seriously overdrawn on his Paterson account, the inventor-entrepreneur recognized that

he was not in a position personally to finance the development of his Submarine Battery, and accordingly he journeyed to Washington early in June 1841. There he established himself at Fuller's Hotel, a Pennsylvania Avenue hostelry that was soon to be immortalized in the derisive prose of Charles Dickens. Having some fourteen months earlier been exasperated by the manner in which a trial lot of his tinfoil cartridges had been fabricated at the Washington Arsenal, Colt deliberately avoided approaching the government through the Army Ordnance Office, which customarily conducted trials of weapons systems offered for official consideration.[34]

Initially, Colt disclosed the details of his mine warfare system to Senator Samuel L. Southard of New Jersey (Figure 18), previously Secretary of the Navy under Presidents James Monroe and John Quincy Adams and currently occupying the strategic position of President of the Senate; and to Major William Gibbs McNeill, formerly of the U.S. Army Corps of Topographical Engineers. Southard, who had earlier brought his inventive constituent's repeating firearms to the attention of the Navy Department, was impressed by his claim that the Submarine Battery was capable of accurately mining a *moving* man-of-war from considerable distance by means of a galvanic impulse. Eschewing an approach via the Ordnance Office, Senator Southard thereupon wrote to President John Tyler directly in behalf of Colt's mechanical ingenuity. Encouraged by this well-placed support,

---

Figure 17.—THE SALVAGE OF THE *Royal George.* In August 1839, the Corps of Royal Sappers and Miners of the British Army, under the direction of Colonel Commandant Charles William Pasley, undertook the removal of the wreck of the 100-gun *Royal George,* which had sunk at Spithead in 1782, seriously obstructing the approaches to Portsmouth. Based on the frigate hulk *Success,* this extended training operation marked the beginning of modern marine salvage. Utilizing two "lumps" moored over the wreck as diving platforms, two rival teams of salvagers outfitted in Siebe's steel-helmeted diving suits methodically dismantled this dangerous hulk. Operations were periodically punctuated by the galvanic detonation of demolition charges ranging from 45 to 2320 pounds of gunpowder. Concluded in 1844, the salvage of the *Royal George* was wholly funded by the sale of her guns and other artifacts at public auction. Meanwhile, as early as December 1839, Pasley's system of galvanic demolitions had been employed in clearing the wreck of the barque *Equitable* from the river approaches to Calcutta, half way round the world.

Figure 18.—SAMUEL LEWIS SOUTHARD, 1787–1842. This veteran Whig jurist graduated from the College of New Jersey in 1804, studied law at Fredericksburg, served as a county prosecutor in Virginia, and in 1815 had been appointed an associate justice of the New Jersey Supreme Court. In 1820, following the election of his friend, James Monroe, Southard received an interim appointment to the United States Senate, where he subsequently played a significant role in the drafting of the Missouri Compromise.

Judge Southard's appointment in 1823 as Secretary of the Navy began a vigorous and progressive administration of that Department that was continued under Monroe's successor, President John Quincy Adams. A strong advocate of a comprehensive naval criminal code, Southard played a pioneering role in identifying the Navy's long-range institutional needs and sought practical measures for reform of the sea services. In 1825 Secretary Southard launched a long-range program for improvement of the Navy's shore establishment, particularly its shipyards. In addition to establishing the first naval hospitals, he promoted construction of the Navy's first dry docks, at Boston and Norfolk. Many of Southard's proposals, such as the founding of a naval academy, organization of a naval exploring expedition, and re-establishment of the National Coast Survey, came to fruition following the Jacksonian avalanche that temporarily swept him from office in 1829.

Returning to law practice in Trenton, Southard won the Governorship in 1832 and subsequently campaigned successfully for the United States Senate. While serving as president of the Senate in 1841–42, Southard took an interest in Samuel Colt's Submarine Battery proposals. Fully appreciative of the Navy's role in the nation's coastal defense program—having early advocated the construction of steam warships for harbor defense—Southard quite evidently failed to impress upon his enterprising constituent the wisdom of advocating his mine warfare system as an auxiliary element in the nation's total defense system. With Southard's death on 2 May 1842 Colt lost his most potent political support.

Colt thereupon wrote to the White House on 19 June, informing the Chief Executive (see also Appendix 1) that

> for more than five years past I have employed my leisure, in study & experiment, to perfect the invention of which I now consider myself master; & which if adopted for the service of our Government, will not only save them millions outlay for the construction of means of defence, but in the event of foreign war, it will prove a perfect safeguard against all the combined fleets of Europe, without exposing the life of our citizens.[35]

In advancing this argument for the economy of his system of coastal defense, Colt invited the President's attention to the publication in 1834, in the first volume of the *American State Papers: Naval Affairs*, of Robert Fulton's mine warfare experiments at New York in 1810, demonstrating the destructive effect of torpedoes detonated beneath wooden vessels.[36] "That discovery," Colt confided to the President, "laid the foundation for my present plan of harbour defence ...."[37] Although cautious in adverting to the unique character of his own system, the inventor was by no means restrained in describing its potential effectiveness:

> Discoveries since Fulton's time combined with an invention original with myself, enable me to effect the instant destruction of either Ships, or Steamers, at my pleasure on their entering a harbour, whether singly or in whole fleets; while those vessels to which I am disposed to allow a passage, are secure from a possibility of being injured. All this I can do in perfect security, & without giving an invading enemy the slightest sign of his danger.
>
> The whole expense of protecting a Harbour like that of New York, would be less then [than] the cost of a single steam ship, & when once prepared, one single man is sufficient to manage the destroying agent against any fleet that Europe can send.[38]

By way of proof, Colt proposed a demonstration of his system before the Cabinet, requesting an appropriation of $20,000 to cover his expenses and, in the event of successful completion of the experiment, payment of an unspecified annuity "as a premium for my secret." This candidly commercial proposal won no early response from the White House, for Tyler, having but recently ascended to the Presidency following the death of William Henry Harrison, was deeply preoccupied with the problem of reaching an understanding with Henry Clay and the Whig majority in Congress on the re-establishment of a sound national fiscal policy. It was in these circumstances that Colt, through the assistance of Senator Southard, an active Clay supporter, finally secured a

brief interview with the President and Secretary of the Navy George E. Badger, to whom the inventor subsequently divulged the essential details of his Submarine Battery. The Tyler administration, having inherited an unprecedented national debt and an unbalanced budget, was in no mood for major expenditures on unproven systems of defense, indeed being obliged during 1841 to suspend the pay of both the military and the civil service on several occasions. Thus, although evidently intrigued by Colt's scheme, Secretary Badger rejected his suggestion that adequate trials might be financed by resort to Navy Department contingency funds.[39]

While Southard undertook to provide for the experiment in forthcoming naval appropriations, Colt now seriously considered an attractive alternative —the proposal by members of a Russian naval commission then studying naval technology in the United States that he place his inventive talents at the service of Tsar Nicholas I. The Russian ambassador, Count Alexander de Bodisco, had earlier evinced considerable interest in Colt's repeating arms. That the Russian commission, headed by Captain Ivan Ivanovich von Schantz,[40] may have been interested in more than revolvers and carbines was indirectly suggested when, on 8 July 1841, the 26-year-old inventor pointedly advised Southard that

> I have had an invitation to go to Russia in the Steam Ship of War [steam frigate *Kamchatka*], built here for the Russian Government. This Steamer will sail about the middle of next month, and should I not meet with satisfactory encouragement from our Government, I shall avail myself of this favorable opportunity to go Abroad: therefore it is of vast importance that my case should be immediately decided, that unless some inducement should be offered for me to remain at home, I shall at once be enabled to commence preparations for my departure.

While such candor had by no means a disarming effect, it was scarcely a unique approach in that speculative era. In the summer of 1834, the British government had been confronted by a somewhat similar proposition in the form of "Warner's Destroyer," an ephemeral underwater ordnance scheme alleged by its inventor, Samuel A. Warner, to be capable of destroying any fleet and rendering modern fortifications obsolete. With notably ill grace, Warner threatened in 1841 to make his invention public if his demands in the amount of £400,000 for purchase of the patent were not met. As for Samuel Colt, he was characteristically direct in appealing anew to his Senator:

I wish you to converse with the President, the Secretary of the Navy and the Chairman of the Naval Committee of the House of Representatives on the subject of my proposition for an exhibition of my Submarine Battery, and inform me what are my prospects of favor with our Government.

It is my wish to give my own country the exclusive use of my discovery, and nothing but actual want will induce me to seek patronage from foreign Governments.

If our Government will but accept my proposition or propose to me any terms that will enable me to obtain the means necessary to make the Exhibition I propose, I will decline the invitation I have received to go abroad.[41]

Unknown to Samuel Colt and doubtless most military authorities in Western Europe, Russia was indeed already well advanced in the application of galvanic technology to undersea warfare. In October 1839, a Russian armed services Committee on Underwater Experiments had been established at St. Petersburg and, under the direction of Professor Moritz von Jacobi (Figure 19), a distinguished member of the Imperial Academy of Sciences, had begun a sustained program of sea mine development. Perhaps spurred by Colonel Charles William Pasley's widely reported galvanic demolitions in England, that committee had as early as 1843 evolved systems of remarkably sophisticated electrical contact mines, as well as of independent "pyrotechnic" mines fired by chemical contact devices. The former observation mine system, destined to be extensively deployed for the defense of Kronstadt during the Crimean War, involved the control of large minefields from inconspicuous command posts whose observers, as in Colt's scheme, might permit the passage of friendly vessels by disconnecting their batteries.

The Russian mines, instantly lethal in darkness or fog, afforded round-the-clock deterrence. Unlike the American system, which involved selective firing of mine clusters from exposed observation posts, the Jacobi system encompassed scores of mines individually fitted with mercury "connecting devices" that permitted the closure of each mine's firing circuit only on its being struck by a passing vessel.[42] Under such circumstances, it is doubtful that Samuel Colt's Submarine Battery would have significantly altered the course of Russian mine warfare development. Aside from the capability of initiating mine explosions for deterrent effect, the American's system offered little of an innovative character with relation to those being developed at St. Petersburg.

Unlike his Swedish contemporary, Immanuel Nobel, the Yankee entrepreneur was not destined to establish himself on the banks of the Neva.[43] Through

the continued efforts of Senator Southard, the naval appropriation bill submitted to Congress early in the fall of 1841 included the provision of $50,000 for naval ordnance development, an allocation understood by both Southard and Secretary Badger to

Figure 19.—MORITZ HERMANN VON JACOBI, 1801–1874. Born at Potsdam, Prussia, Jacobi studied architecture at Göttingen and, following a brief practice in Königsberg, became Professor of Architecture in 1835 at the University of Dorpat (Tartu), long a center of Germanic academic influence in Russia. Jacobi's scientific interests, stimulated by his study of J. Frederic Daniell's "constant" galvanic battery, led him to St. Petersburg two years later as a junior associate in the Imperial Academy of Sciences and subsequently resulted in his appointment as a regular member of the academy in 1847.

In addition to numerous pioneering contributions to electro-mechanics, telegraphy, and metallurgy, Jacobi served for many years as member of the Council on Manufactures in the Russian Ministry of Finance. His notable contributions as scientific member of the armed services Committee of Underwater Experiments from 1839 to 1856 fairly qualify Academician Jacobi as the father of Russian mine-warfare technology. Being convinced of the necessity for maintaining absolute secrecy regarding his galvanic mine developments, he deliberately refrained from publishing scientific treatises on that subject.

include planned experiments with the Submarine Battery. Unfortunately for Colt, this gentleman's agreement was suddenly vitiated by the dramatic resignation on 10 September of Tyler's entire Cabinet, excepting Secretary of State Daniel Webster, at the climax of mounting Whig outrage with the President's conservative fiscal policies.[44]

Colt may not have initially grasped the implications of this violent political upheaval for early adoption of his mine warfare system, owing doubtless to his increasing preoccupation with a family tragedy involving the trial of his elder brother John for murder. While Sam hastened to New York for costly legal efforts in behalf of the accused, Major William

Figure 20.—UNIVERSITY OF THE CITY OF NEW YORK. Opened some three years after the University's founding in 1832, the Gothic "old main" on the east side of Washington Square was aptly described by Theodore Winthrop as "half college and half lodging house" in its early years. Artists, inventors, and literary figures not on the University staff soon moved into the upper floors, supplementing the young institution's slender financial resources.

As Henry James later wrote, "The ideal of quiet and genteel retirement, in 1835, was found in Washington Square." Samuel Colt secured rooms in the University's south tower in 1841, soon making the acquaintance of both Morse and Professor John William Draper, a distinguished chemist and long a mainstay of the medical school. With their occasional assistance, Colt set up a modest laboratory and during 1842–44 conducted a series of materials tests for elements of his Submarine Battery, exchanging insulated cable with Morse and at times utilizing the Professor's own remarkable laboratory.

G. McNeill attempted unsuccessfully to secure a more active consideration of the Submarine Battery by Tyler's new Secretary of the Navy, Judge Abel P. Upshur, a Tidewater Virginian who well exemplified the fiscal conservatism of the second Tyler Cabinet.[45] The persuasive Colt, however, was not long to be denied. Returning to Washington midway in November 1841, the inventor provided Upshur an account of his previous experiments (Appendix 2), invited the Secretary's attention to Thomas Jefferson's little-known benediction on Robert Fulton's earlier torpedo warfare proposals, and, finally securing an interview with Upshur, "went over with him the whole plans and secrets of my inventions which so far convinced him of their practicability that to remove the only remaining doubt he simply required me to make the single experiment of the blowing up of a vessel at a distance beyond the range of an enemy's shot." [46]

While impressed by Colt's conception, Upshur provided him no *carte blanche*, offering no commitment regarding an eventual premium. He did, however, authorize a working advance of $6,000 for a sharply limited demonstration of the Submarine Battery principle, one that virtually eliminated the observation features of that system. More surprisingly, the Secretary did not submit Colt's proposal to the Board of Navy Commissioners for evaluation, a well-established advisory procedure that Upshur evidently felt constrained to waive, owing to the injunction of secrecy with which the inventor presented his case. For his part, Colt submitted no patent application at this juncture, most probably a reflection of both the relatively undeveloped state of the Submarine Battery idea and his determination to avoid an early critique of that system by military professionals. Even a modest advance from the Navy Department constituted official support for development of his conception, however, and the young manufacturer, characteristically grasping an advantage, gratuitously advised Upshur on 24 November:

By stating in your annual report that Secret experiments are being made which may result in a Material change in our present System of Harbour & Coast Defence & that you will make a Special report of their Success for the information of Congress, at as early a period as possible, you will undoubtedly prepare them for an immediate and favourable action, whenever the matter is brought up for their decision.[47]

At first glance, Colt had chosen wisely in not making his initial overtures to Congress by way of the War Department, whose Corps of Engineers was deeply committed to its massive program of coastal fortifications. Owing to his earlier disappointments at the hands of the Army Ordnance Office, Colt exercised exceptional caution in his subsequent relations with military professionals, prophetically and most revealingly warning Senator Southard regarding the nascent Submarine Battery that "if . . . the story is told or sufficient of it to excite the jealousy of the officers of the Army & Navy (particularly that portion of them that are exeld in putting togeather stone and morter) the invention will be still born into oblivion & what has been so well begun will neather proffit ourselves or be worth anything." [48]

With Navy Department support formally confirmed on 25 November 1841, the inventor-entrepreneur moved rapidly to acquire additional financing from the private sector and began testing necessary elements of his galvanic mine warfare system in laboratories at the University of the City of New York (Figure 20), located at Washington Square. [49] Stock certificates for the "Submarine Battery Company," formed on 18 December 1841, were printed to a capitalization of $100,000, and a handful of subscribers, including both Senator Southard and Major McNeill, were secured, thus adding an unmistakably speculative dimension to this governmentally sponsored venture.[50] In an effort to assure professional naval support, Colt thereupon initiated correspondence in behalf of McNeill's appointment as Chief Engineer of the Navy Department, a maneuver that was destined to prove unsuccessful. The Navy's steam engineers, currently involved in a crucial struggle to achieve full professional stature within the service, were about to secure Congressional reorganization of their Engineer Corps and succeeded methodically in frustrating McNeill's aspirations.[51]

Experiments and Demonstrations

Every thing on my part was conducted as privately as possible so much so that every reporter for [the New York] newspapers have as yet mistaken even the place I were stationed when I made the explosion.

SAMUEL COLT TO SECRETARY OF THE NAVY ABEL P. UPSHUR,
NEW YORK, 19 OCTOBER 1842

During the winter of 1841–42, Colt was engaged in the procurement, insulation and testing of several thousand feet of rolled copper wire, whose manufacture was undertaken at the Waterbury works of Philo Brown and John P. Elton.[52] At this juncture Colt began consulting with his Washington Square neighbors, Professors John William Draper and Samuel F. B. Morse, the latter (Figure 21), then living in genteel poverty while perfecting his electro-magnetic telegraph. From Draper, an able physicist, Colt learned the Hare system of galvanic detonation. Morse was particularly interested in Colt's efforts to secure insulated cable that was capable of transmitting electric current relatively undiminished for substantial distances.[53] Morse's interest was doubtless particularly heightened in March 1842, when Colt reported to Secretary Upshur his success in firing a gunpowder charge some ten miles distant from his battery.[54] The subsequent active collaboration between these two inventors is well reflected in Morse's midyear letter to Professor Joseph Henry of the College of New Jersey at Princeton:

During the last few months I have availed myself of the means which Mr. Samuel Colt has had at his command in experimenting with wire circuits for testing his submarine batteries; also to test some very important matters in relation to the Telegraph. I loaned him, in the first instance, my two reels of wire, which . . . is reduced to eight and a quarter miles . . . . The experiments were highly satisfactory, the magnetism and the heating effects, which latter Mr. Colt desired, being apparently stronger when the wire was stretched out than when in coil. We also found that when one wire was coated, the other might be naked, and passed to any distance.

This result induced Mr. Colt to contract for his purposes, for the purchase of forty miles of wire . . . . Twenty miles have already been finished, and we have experimented with perfectly satisfactory results on this distance.[55]

Notwithstanding preoccupation early in 1842 with the impending trial of John Colt, as well as his experiments at Washington Square, Sam took time to journey to New London, Stonington, and Mystic to investigate several intriguing leads on the attempts of an obscure Connecticut inventor, Silas Clowden Halsey, to conduct a torpedo attack against British warships blockading New London in 1814. Although interested enough to sketch out oral descriptions that he secured of Halsey's one-man submersible and towing torpedo,[56] Colt was evidently even more anxious to document the motive for such lone ventures, which was found in emergency legislation enacted by Congress on 3 March 1813, offering rewards for the destruction of British blockading vessels. Adopted in a mood of revulsion following outrages committed by British amphibious forces at Hampton, Virginia, this legislation reflected a virtual bankruptcy of national military resources.

Be it enacted, &c., That, during the present war with Great Britain, it shall be lawful for any persons to burn, sink, or destroy, any British armed vessel of war, except vessels coming as cartels or flags of truce; and for that purpose to use torpedoes, submarine instruments, or any other destructive machine whatever; and a bounty of one-half the value of the armed vessel so burnt, sunk, or destroyed, and also one-half the value of her guns, cargo, tackle, and apparel, shall be paid out of the Treasury of the United States to such person or persons who shall effect the same, otherwise than by the armed or commissioned vessels of the United States.[57]

As Colt observed to Senator Southard on 13 February 1842: "The fact of the government having to resort to private resources & contrivances at that time to destroy the enemy is I think a strong argument in favour of paying a liberal reward for my invention. . . ."[58]

Press reports from Washington regarding Congres-

22

Figure 21.—SAMUEL FINLEY BREESE MORSE, 1791–1872. Born at Charlestown, Massachusetts, Morse graduated from Yale in 1810 and subsequently studied painting in London under Washington Allston. Returning to America in 1815, he achieved recognition as a portrait artist and served as first president of the National Academy of Design. Morse was appointed Professor of Sculpture and Painting at the young University of the City of New York in 1835, thereupon acquiring an apartment in that gothic landmark on the east side of Washington Square, where he subsequently developed the principal components of his electromagnetic recording telegraph. At Washington Square he designed both transmitting and receiving apparatus for his telegraph. Upon a suggestion by Leonard D. Gale, who collaborated in devising a signal code, Morse used Joseph Henry's multicell battery and intensity magnet in his telegraph receiver, thus permitting the transmission of messages through ten miles of wire wound about his laboratory. With Henry's encouragement, he devised an electromagnetic renewer or relay, which further extended his transmission capability, leading Morse to file a caveat for his system in 1837 at the United States Patent Office. Following a successful public trial of his telegraph at New York, the artist-inventor exhibited it at the Franklin Institute and in 1838 demonstrated its operation to the Cabinet of President Martin Van Buren.

Although frustrated in his hopes for early Congressional appropriations to develop his system, Professor Morse doggedly continued his experiments for the next six years, until his triumphant demonstration of the telegraph at Washington in 1844.

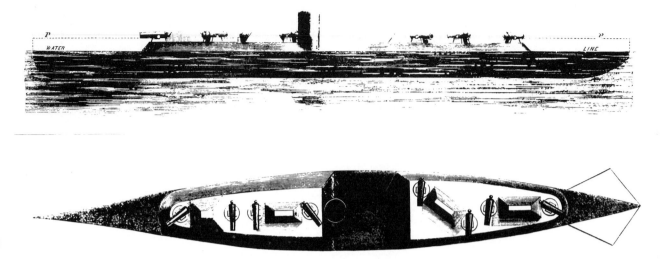

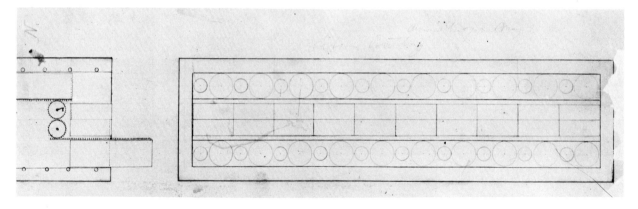

Figure 22.—THE STEVENS BATTERY. Conceived by John Stevens, a pioneer of steam navigation and railways in the United States, this iron-clad harbor defense battery was authorized by Congressional act on 14 April 1842, appropriating an initial $250,000 for construction of "a war steamer, shot and shell proof, to be built principally of iron," in accordance with plans developed by Robert L. and Edwin A. Stevens, sons of its original proponent. Approved by a joint Coast Defense Board consisting of Commodore Charles Stewart, Captain Matthew C. Perry, Colonel Sylvanus Thayer, and Colonel Joseph G. Totten, this floating steam battery was originally designed to measure some 250 feet in length and be fitted with armor plating 4½ inches thick. Ballistics tests against such armor conducted subsequently by the Swedish inventor John Ericsson severely shook official confidence in Washington, and it was not until 1854, when Robert L. Stevens had revised his project to encompass a sharp-lined vessel 420 feet long and with a 53-foot beam, that construction was begun. During the ensuing twenty months, Stevens expended $500,000 in government funds and $200,000 of his own fortune in an unsuccessful effort to finish plating this 6,000-ton vessel.

Naval officials refused to invest government funds to finish the Stevens Battery's 6¾-inch armor during the Civil War, and although an additional $1,000,000 of the Stevens fortune was subsequently invested in the project, Congress refused in 1874 to authorize further funds for its completion. Scrapping of the Stevens Battery shortly thereafter closed a chapter in the early history of American iron-clad construction.

Figure 23.—COLT'S "SIPHON BATTERY," 1842. Drafted at the University of the City of New York in May 1842, this plan for a multicell battery appears to have envisaged an arrangement for raising and lowering plates into two electrolytes by means of geared wheels. Three years later, *The Scientific American,* in describing the more advanced Grove Battery, asserted that "this is the kind of battery that is used in producing the electro-magnetic action in Morse's Telegraph, and for the ignition of Colt's submarine explosive battery." Thus, although initially influenced by the plunge-type arrangement embodied in Robert Hare's calorimotor, Colt appears subsequently to have followed Morse's decision to employ the Grove system (see Figure 30).

sional consideration of Robert L. Stevens' harbor defense battery further roused Colt, leading him to assert to Southard that "the original cost ... will be more than the cost of protecting the port of New York on my plan against the Whole British Navy...."[59] The final passage of legislation appropriating $250,000 for the revolutionary iron-hulled Stevens Battery (Figure 22) proved particularly disturbing, for Colt's own hopes of demonstrating his Submarine Battery at Washington in May 1842 were frustrated by the evident incapacity of his Leyden jars to provide current sufficient for more than a single mine detonation. This lead him to dispatch an urgent requisition to Brown and Elton for "250 plates of Zinc four & a half inches wide, twelve & a half inches long and one eighth of an inch thick."[60] Described by Colt as "siphon batteries" (Figure 23), the voltage sources constructed by the inventor for his ensuing experiment appear to have been of a multicell, plunge type, possibly incorporating the constant voltage characteristics of J. Frederic Daniell's two-electrolyte cell, which, as adapted in 1838 by William R. Grove, was subsequently to be employed by Samuel F. B. Morse in his telegraph experiments.[61]

Continued delays in the delivery of various elements of the Submarine Battery proved disquieting for both Colt and the Navy Department, obliging Secretary Upshur to suspend further warrants to his account in the spring of 1842. Nevertheless, through the timely assistance of the Commandant of the New York Navy Yard, Captain Matthew C. Perry (Figure 24), who had on 4 June observed a private trial of Colt's galvanic detonating system, the 27-year-old entrepreneur finally secured sufficient gunpowder to undertake an initial public demonstration of his Submarine Battery in New York Harbor, characteristically on the Fourth of July 1842.[62] Colt, who had earlier sought both state and local interest in his system for the defense of New York, made the most of the National Jubilee. By way of securing maximum public exposure, as well as obtaining additional funding for his experiments, he made arrangements to conduct the Submarine Battery demonstration directly off Castle Garden, a popular open-air theater located in venerable Castle Clinton on lower Manhattan, the scene less than two years earlier of a demonstration of "Cochran's Bomb Cannon," another transient ordnance phenomenon of the era.[63] Aware of the national attention galvanized by such exhibitions, Colt dispatched a round of invitations to the New

Figure 24.—MATTHEW CALBRAITH PERRY, 1794–1858. A native of Newport, this younger brother of Commodore Oliver Hazard Perry entered the Navy as a midshipman in 1809, was wounded three years later during the engagement between the *President* and H.M.S. *Belvidera* and subsequently served in the Caribbean patrol against West Indian pirates. An officer of notable vision, who is best remembered for his successful role in establishing trade relations with Japan, Perry had successfully advocated the establishment of a naval apprentice system and took a leading role in promoting the creation of the Navy's Engineer Corps. As commanding officer of the U.S.S. *Fulton II,* he trained a rising generation of American naval engineers, being indeed regarded as the father of the steam Navy of the United States.

York press. To his delight, his experiment received generous notice, the New York *Evening Post* relating that

an interesting experiment with Colt's sub-marine battery created much attention, and was witnessed by many thousands with great satisfaction. An old hulk was moored off Castle Garden fitted with temporary masts, from which were displayed various flags, with piratical devices, immediately under which the battery was placed, and the effect of the explosions was tremendous. The vessel was shattered into fragments, some of which were thrown two or three hundred feet in the air, and there was not a single piece left longer than a man could have carried in one hand.[64]

The theatrical effects may have been intended on this occasion to divert close press scrutiny of Colt's firing arrangements, whose exact character yet remains uncertain, owing to conflicting reports. Several observers noted merely a simple demolition on a motionless target, obviating any need for the distinctive observation post features of the Submarine Battery system. Particularly direct on this score was an account by the New York *American*:

The case containing the combustibles was sunk under the hulk, and a wire conducted from it to the deck of the *North Carolina*, distant some two or three hundred yards. At the moment fixed, (1 o'clock) Mr. Colt, on the deck of the *Carolina*, applied the acid to his plates, and quicker than thought, the doomed hulk was thrown into the air....[65]

The inventor, who had conducted his experiment on board the 74-gun *North Carolina* through the courtesy of Captain Francis H. Gregory, provided a more impressive account of his achievement to the Navy Department, asserting that his target "was being towed through the water at the rate of about three knots an hour."[66] This assertion was indeed corroborated by the report of the New York *Herald*: "The battery having been placed under her bottom, the cable of the doomed vessel was cut, & when by the aid of the tide and the boats of the United States' Ship *North Carolina*, her speed through the water had been made about four knots an hour, the explosion took place...."[67] That Colt may have employed an unusually long lead from his battery to a charge affixed to the target vessel's hull cannot be dismissed lightly. Secretary of the Navy Upshur received no official report from Captain Gregory or Captain Perry, and it is conceivable that he did not read the judgment of the New York *Sun*, subsequently reprinted by *Niles' National Register*:

Any thing less than a ship of the line must have been either destroyed or capsized had the explosion taken place

immediately under it. But it strikes us that the great difficulty in rendering the battery efficient must be the impossibility of placing it immediately under any vessel that it may be designed to destroy.[68]

Notwithstanding puzzling contradictions, Samuel Colt's exhibition at New York had effectively focused national attention on his Submarine Battery, inducing Secretary Upshur to renew cautious encouragement to the entrepreneur's maturing plans for conducting a more complete demonstration at Washington, in the presence of the Congress.[69] Recognizing the critical importance of this second trial, Colt urged that it be solidly supported with the remainder of the original $50,000 appropriation for ordnance experiments, assuring the Virginian on 5 July that

I will guarantee to fortify every Port upon our Seaboard against the combined Fleets of Europe, at a cost for each, less than that required to build a single steam ship of war; and when once fixed, my Engine of destruction may be used without the expense of fuel or soldiers, the cost of which, every year, exceeds the expense of making permanent Fortifications of my construction.[70]

Unfortunately for Colt, then desperately organizing legal efforts in behalf of his accused brother, government support proved insufficient at this juncture to permit a thorough evaluation of the Submarine Battery by responsible authorities. Secretary Upshur, who routinely referred new weapons proposals to his overburdened Board of Navy Commissioners for testing by naval ordnance specialists or officers of the Ordnance Office of the Army, took no steps to arrange a trial of Colt's mine warfare system by military professionals, again evidently in deference to the inventor's insistence on secrecy in the matter.[71]

The Navy, then anticipating a major administrative reorganization, initiated by Upshur, that was to see the Board of Navy Commissioners replaced by the bureau system in September 1842, still lacked a permanent weapons-testing establishment, comparable to the Army's Ordnance Office, within which a complex system of armament might receive comprehensive evaluation and possibly be subjected to further development. While awaiting Senate action on his proposed reorganization of the Navy Department, Upshur had felt obliged on 11 July to reject Colt's request for the purchase of a sizable target vessel for the Washington demonstration, indicating instead his intention of laying the matter before Congress.[72] Meanwhile the death of Senator Southard late in June had deprived Colt of critically strategic support on Capitol Hill,[73] and it soon became apparent to the entrepreneur upon his arrival in Washington on 2 August that strong opposition to his mine warfare proposal was developing in the House of Representatives. That opposition centered notably in the person of John Quincy Adams. The venerable ex-President, who did not share Southard's confidence in the practicality of Colt's harbor defense scheme, further strongly objected to it on moral grounds and adamantly ignored the inventor's request on 11 August for an interview on the matter.[74]

Far more disturbing for Colt's Submarine Battery prospects, however, was the dissipation of the prolonged threat of hostilities with Great Britain in the summer of 1842, almost coincidentally with the conclusion of the Seminole War and resulting Congressional reduction of the Regular Army. As the well-informed Adams had learned on 24 July from the British minister plenipotentiary, Lord Ashburton, extended negotiations between that diplomat and Secretary of State Daniel Webster on the disputed Maine boundary had been substantially and amicably concluded, affording Congress the welcomed prospect of adjournment before fall.[75]

Discovering that time had nearly run out, Colt and his assistant, Robert Cummings, hastened preparations for the Washington demonstration. Colt began the difficult cable-laying operations on 11 August with a boat crew and carpenter from the Navy Yard and employed their services for no fewer than three weeks, both in laying and later recovering reels of insulated cable from the United States Arsenal at Greenleaf Point to a firing station some five miles distant on the Alexandria waterfront. On 18 August Colt secured Secretary Upshur's permission to spend upwards of $150 for a target vessel—which the inventor described as a sixty-ton schooner—and further requested surplus spars, masts, rigging, and a supply of gunpowder. Upshur referred the powder request to Lt. Col. George Talcott of the Army Ordnance Office, while calling on Captain Beverly Kennon, Commandant of the Washington Navy Yard, for available ship stores. Kennon took a dim view of Colt's venture, sternly advising:

We have no condemned materials on hand in the yard suitable for rigging the temporary masts referred to . . . there is no rigging even suitable. The only rubbish in the yard is a quantity of empty beer barrels, which will be furnished.[76]

Beer barrels were rarely scorned by early submarine miners, yet Colt later caustically informed the Navy Department that "the cost of *hack hire* (to say nothing of personal annoyance & waste of time) was far greater than the advantage I derived from the Washington Navy Yard." [77] Subsequent events suggest that, although clearly pressed for time, Colt would have rejected close collaboration by military or naval ordnance specialists, for fear of disclosing to them the exact nature of his firing arrangements. Having deployed his curious equipage—galvanic batteries, firing controls, fathoms of insulated cable and the mystery-shrouded "infernal machine"—with the assistance of Navy Yard ordinarymen, Colt dispatched his characteristic announcements to the press. Time was indeed running out for the inventor. Even as Colt undertook his first Washington demonstration on the evening of 20 August off Greenleaf Point, the Senate found itself locked in a lengthy debate that culminated about nine o'clock in formal ratification of the Webster-Ashburton Treaty,[78] terminating the threat of Anglo-American hostilities.

Few records survive to document Colt's final arrangements on the Potomac, but it is evident that, while securing limited materials and manual labor from official sources, he carefully avoided professional participation by either the capital's military or scientific community. If he again considered filing a patent petition to protect his Submarine Battery scheme at this juncture, he appears to have rejected the notion as premature. As subsequently became clear, months of materials development and testing lay ahead before Colt would be prepared to demonstrate his entire mining system in the most rudimentary form. While instrumental in providing gunpowder, barrels, workboats, and laborers, neither the Army Ordnance Office or the Board of Navy Commissioners appear to have been consulted by Colt, notwithstanding the fact that his demonstration was staged off the U.S. Arsenal for the edification of the Cabinet, the Congress, and "an immense concourse of spectators." [79]

No less remarkable was Colt's failure to consult members of that short-lived forerunner of the Smithsonian Institution, the National Institute for the Promotion of Science, whose headquarters were lodged in the capital's impressive new Patent Office (Figure 25).[80] Founded in May 1840 through the efforts of then Secretary of the Navy Joel R. Poinsett and other prominent federal officials, this transient association (originally designated the National Institution but from mid-1842 styled the National Institute) had briefly emerged as a potential institutional recipient of the indenture of James Smithson, that

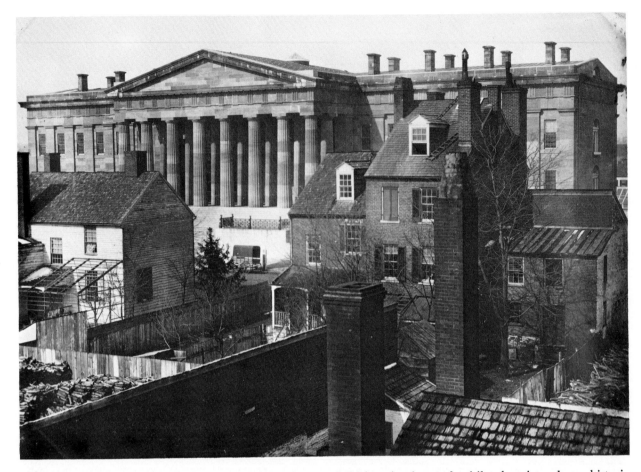

Figure 25.—THE UNITED STATES PATENT OFFICE, CA. 1846. This classic marble structure, begun in 1836 following the destruction of the original Patent Office by fire, was completed in 1840. In addition to housing several government bureaus including the Patent Office, it became the repository of four museum collections, including major exhibits from the Wilkes and Perry expeditions, the varied acquisitions of the National Institute for the Promotion of Science, and miscellaneous donations from individuals. Its exhibits included Franklin's cane and printing press; Washington's sword, uniform, field chest, and campaign tent; and the memorabilia of James Smithson—national treasures subsequently to be incorporated in the collection of the Smithsonian Institution.

Here the National Institute briefly had its headquarters, and here, ironically, Samuel Colt stored substantial elements of his Submarine Battery equipment, following his demonstration of August 1842, evidently in a basement chamber judging from his subsequent correspondence with Henry L. Ellsworth, the sympathetic Commissioner of Patents. Colt ultimately submitted his application for a patent on the Submarine Battery on 8 June 1844, only to withdraw it the following day in a mood of evidently mounting outrage.

British scientist and philanthropist whose historic bequest of some $515,000 to the United States had been formally received by Congress in 1836 for the stipulated if highly challenging purpose of founding "an establishment for the increase and diffusion of knowledge among men." [81]

By the eventful summer of 1842, the National Institute had secured the sympathetic patronage of President Tyler, established correspondence with some 150 scientific societies in Europe and North America, and was taking steps to acquire a major scientific collection brought back from the Pacific in 1841 by Lieutenant Charles Wilkes' United States Exploring Expedition. Acquisition of the Wilkes Collection accorded well with the National Institute's declared object, "to promote science and the useful arts, and to establish a national museum of natural history. . . ." [82] During the summer of 1842, it may further be noted, the War and Navy Departments had issued circulars to ships and shore commands encouraging the establishment of scientific cabinets suitable for preserving collections ultimately destined for the National Institute.[83] Stimulated by the example of both Secretary Poinsett and Secretary of War Levi Woodbury, several scientifically inclined officers in the armed services had assumed active roles in the National Institute, notably including Lieutenant Matthew Fontaine Maury, Officer-in-Charge of the Navy's Depot of Charts and Instruments, and Colonel Joseph G. Totten, Chief of the Army's Corps of Engineers and for practical purposes the director of the nation's growing system of coastal fortifications. At first glance, an association such as the National Institute, potentially a national academy of sciences, might have proven a suitable womb within which Samuel Colt's remarkable system could have developed. In reality, however, the presence of Colonel Totten and, until quite recently, Representative John Quincy Adams on the Institute's Board of Directors, appears to have dissuaded Colt, who had himself been enrolled as a corresponding member of the Institute as early as August 1840, from attempting to avail himself of that association's support in the development of his Submarine Battery.[84]

Thus it was that Colt eschewed conducting his first Washington experiment in the privacy of an ordnance proving ground, preferring once again to stage a simple public demonstration which, while generating powerful political impetus for his proposal, permitted the inventor to conceal the precise character of his underwater system. Contemporary accounts of this second Submarine Battery trial, conducted on 20 August before some 8,000 spectators congregated at the Washington Arsenal (Figure 26), indicate that Colt carried out a somewhat more sophisticated demolition of a moored target, described by the New York *Evening Post* as "an Accomac clam boat." [85]

At half past five, the steamer containing the President and members of the cabinet, with their suites, was opposite the spectators, and its illustrious and precious freight received a very hearty greeting from the mouths of twenty-four great guns. A few minutes afterwards the signal for the explosion was given by the discharge of a twenty-four pounder, and instantaneously, as though a missile from the gun itself had borne the torch to a magazine in her, the old craft was sent in ten millions of fragments five hundred feet into the air, and then fell into the water with a roar like that of Niagara . . . .[86]

An observant reporter of the Washington *Daily National Intelligencer* ascertained that Colt's target had been moored about 150 yards offshore, asserting that "the case of combustibles" had been placed underneath the target, on the bottom of the river." [87]

Whether Colt's explosive device was laid as a ground mine or anchored, as indicated in his patent drawings, remains obscure. Colt's success in frustrating close analysis of his system is indicated by the same reporter's statement that

the charge placed beneath the vessel is said to have been exploded by the inventor or discoverer of the power, he being at Alexandria, five miles off when the signal was given, by means of dipping into an acid the ends of a magnetic wire communicating with the charge. If this be true, it must be a sure and absolute defense for all our harbors which are approached through narrow channels.[88]

Having visually confirmed the complete destruction of Colt's target vessel off the arsenal, the Presidential party steamed down the Potomac to his mine control station at Alexandria, having ample opportunity to consider the impunity with which his device had wrought its destructive result "at a distance far beyond the reach of guns of the largest calibre." [89] Remarkably enough, there is no evidence that members of Tyler's suite went ashore to examine the inventor's galvanic apparatus. Colt was instead invited on board, roundly congratulated, and presented a bouquet by the Chief Executive's daughter that provided a long-treasured memento of this strikingly social occasion.[90] Secretary of the Navy Upshur appears to have been satisfied by Colt's simple demonstration, leading him to forward a request to the Chairman of the House Committee on Naval Affairs, Representative Henry A. Wise, that an expression of Congressional opinion would be appropriate if further trials of the Submarine Battery were desired.[91] The inventor, however, had something more concrete in mind. On 23 August, in response to Colt's own request, Representative Edward Stanly introduced a joint resolution in the House, instructing the Secretary of the Navy

to render Mr. Samuel Colt facilities to test his submarine battery to an extent, which will settle the questions whether there can, with ease and safety, successfully be employed a power sufficient to destroy the largest class of ships of war, when in motion, passing in or out of harbor, without the necessity of approach within reach of shot from guns of the largest calibre; and whether continuous operations, after the destruction of one or more vessels, can be effected without removing the means under exposure to an advancing squadron; and whether the same can be used for the defense of a harbor, without endangering the passage in or out of other than hostile vessels.[92]

In support of this portion of Stanly's motion, Representative Wise emphasized that such additional Navy

Figure 26.—THE WASHINGTON ARSENAL, CA. 1861. Erected at Greenleaf Point, on the ruins of magazines destroyed by British forces during the burning of Washington in 1814, the Washington Arsenal was described by Colonel George Bomford in 1841, as "an arsenal of construction, advantageously situated for making and preserving patterns, inspecting instruments and models, as well as for building artillery-carriages, &c."

Although in no sense a gun foundry, the arsenal was the scene of periodic ordnance experiments. In the spring of 1841, Samuel Colt secured permission from Lt. Col. George Talcott of the Ordnance Office to demonstrate the hand manufacture of tinfoil cartridges of his own design at the arsenal, employing a guard made available by the officer in charge. To his chagrin, the inventor "found that the man whom I had taught to make my cartridges, had been kept on guard all day & night preceding & not relieved until seven o'clock in the morning.... As usually happens in such cases, he took his revenge upon my cartridges." This experience, followed ultimately by government cancellation of a small contract for his tinfoil cartridges, confirmed Colt's growing disillusionment with the Ordnance Office of the War Department. Significantly, when the inventor first tested his galvanic mining system at Washington in August 1842, he personally avoided recourse to the Ordnance Board, while conducting his demolition directly off the Washington Arsenal.

Department assistance was authorized under previous legislation in 1841 allocating $50,000 for ordnance experiments. Mindful of other submarine warfare proposals, notably George W. Taylor's "submarine rocket," Wise was unprepared to support Stanly's further recommendation that the Navy Department be authorized to conclude contracts with Colt for actual installation of Submarine Batteries in a selected harbor, asserting that "he thought he understood from the Secretary of the Navy the nature of Mr. Colt's invention, and it was not necessary to lay down the shells in time of peace." [93]

Congress was now moving rapidly toward adjournment, but it was apparent to John Quincy Adams that Colt's spectacular demonstration had powerfully influenced Congressional opinion. The doughty ex-President advised the House that he was convinced that further experiments "would be but the throwing of so much money into the sea."

He was as fully conscious that the system would be useless to the United States, as if one hundred years had passed; but if it could be made successful, he was opposed to blowing up ships of war with submarine batteries; if done at all, it should be done by fair and honest warfare.[94]

Notwithstanding Adams' strong opposition, the House passed the Submarine Battery resolution on 25 August 1842, by a vote of 108 to 51, in effect confirming the opinion of the departed Southard.[95] As ultimately hammered out in conference with the Senate, this joint resolution appropriated $15,000 from the Navy Department's ordnance experiments fund for Colt's subsequent demonstrations, while allocating $6,000 from that fund for unrelated steam boiler tests. Final action in the Senate was taken within hours of adjournment on 31 August, significantly with the support of John C. Calhoun, under whose leadership some two decades earlier the War Department had inaugurated its massive postwar program of coastal fortifications.[96]

Colt, ever mindful of the verdict approaching in his brother's trial, did not long remain in Washington. Before departing, however, he *may* have paid a visit to the Navy's Depot of Charts and Instruments, then located in modest quarters on Pennsylvania Avenue, armed with an introduction from Secretary Upshur to the new Officer-in-Charge of that establishment, Lieutenant Matthew Fontaine Maury, USN (Figure 27): "I would thank Mr. Maury to allow Mr. Colt to consult such charts as he desires at the Depot." [97] The survival of this intriguing introduction *in the inventor's papers* does not argue persuasively that a meeting did indeed take place between Colt and the Navy's future hydrographer. A chart of the Potomac and Eastern Branch surviving in Colt's Submarine Battery drawings is more convincingly ascribed to his second demonstration in Washington in 1844,[98] yet an encounter between these two seminal figures, however brief and apparently unfruitful, *may* indeed have occurred. Maury, who had recently assumed his duties at the Depot of Charts and Instruments, had already emerged as a leading advocate of naval administrative reform and early expansion of the steam Navy as a major adjunct to coastal defense. He was to achieve international recognition during the ensuing two decades for his pioneer contributions to oceanography and, significantly, played a substantial role in promoting the first trans-Atlantic cable.[99] Ultimately, perhaps with but dim recollection of the Yankee inventor's attempts to secure official acceptance of his mysterious Submarine Battery, Maury was to achieve a grimmer reputation as founder of the Confederate torpedo service at the outset of the American Civil War.[100]

Whether or not Maury ascertained even the most evident characteristics of Colt's system of mine war-

Figure 27.—MATTHEW FONTAINE MAURY, 1806–1873. A native of Virginia, this pioneer American oceanographer entered the United States Navy as a midshipman in 1825 and served at sea until 1834, demonstrating notable talent in navigation and hydrographic surveys. Maury's first professional paper, "On the Navigation of Cape Horn," was published in 1834 in Silliman's *American Journal of Science and Arts,* being followed two years later by his lucid *New Theoretical and Practical Treatise on Navigation,* which won the approval of mariners and scientists alike. Professional differences with Charles Wilkes denied Maury his first great scientific opportunity, that of participating in the United States Exploring Expedition of 1838–1842. Following a stagecoach accident that abruptly ended his seagoing career in 1839, he redeemed months of painful recovery by composing his penetrating "Harry Bluff" articles for *The Southern Literary Messenger,* advocating reforms in naval administration and education that bore fruit within half a decade in the establishment of the bureau system in the Navy Department and of the Naval Academy at Annapolis.

Unable to secure further sea duty, Maury devoted himself to scientific writing, taking an active role in the shortlived National Institute and in 1842 being appointed Officer-in-Charge of the Navy's new Depot of Charts and Instruments at Washington. During his 19 years as head of the Navy's prime scientific establishment, Maury developed its observatory into an institution of world-wide repute, made major contributions to international collaboration in meteorological research, played an important role in locating a suitable submarine plateau for the first trans-Atlantic cable, and won international honors for the contribution which his *Sailing Directions* made to the safety of ocean commerce. In *The Physical Geography of the Sea,* first published in 1854, Maury achieved a remarkable early delineation of the science of oceanography. Such was the distinguished background to Maury's efforts as founder of the Confederate torpedo service early in the Civil War, a conflict that had tragic consequences for his scientific career.

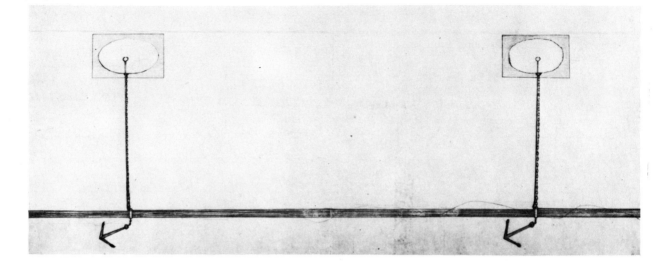

Figure 28.—ANCHORED MINES FOR COLT'S SUBMARINE BATTERY. Anchors, chain, and galvanic cabling appear in inventories of Colt's Submarine Battery equipment in 1844. In this drawing "G," the inventor depicts buoyant mine cases in cross-section, equipped with what appear to be carbon-arc fuses. Individual leads from a submarine cable line run up alongside anchor chain to the mine cases, reflecting Colt's plan for selective firing by the operator, who does not appear to have the benefit of sighting buoys.

fare at this juncture remains a mystery, on which the Virginian's papers shed no light.[101] Notwithstanding Colt's evident desire to avoid close official scrutiny, the inventor or possibly a journalistic friend appears to have unveiled a major portion of his firing system just five weeks later, on the eve of yet another demonstration, in a characteristic flight of prose (Appendix 3) that appeared in the *Alexandria Gazette and Virginia Advertiser* on 5 October 1842, in the form of a "Letter from Washington" under the cryptic authorship of one "C."

I do not know whether you have seen or published an account of Colt's Steam [Submarine] Battery, and as its description is simple and yet interesting, I have transcribed the following from a Northern paper, viz:—the Battery consists of a light sheet iron box filled with gunpowder, and having two copper wires wound around with cotton, then varnished with a mixture of gum shellack, alcohol and Venice Turpentine, and extending through tight corks in one side of the box, having a piece of platina wire extending between them in the box amongst the gunpowder, and the two copper wires extending off from this box (which may be anchored in the channel of a river) to a large one of Grant's Electricity collecting [connecting] machines, electrified by a large Galvanic Battery, which may be seven or eight miles distant from the box, and where the operation [operator] is, having one of the wires in his hand ready to attach them to the collectors [connectors] the instant the signal is given to explode the box.[102]

No description of the Submarine Battery's platinum filament fuse phrased in comparable detail may be found in Colt's subsequent patent petition of 1844 or, indeed, elsewhere in his voluminous correspondence. While this extraordinary public revelation may quite

plausibly be attributed to Colt or an associate on the basis of its caustic and, as it proved, impolitic ensuing comments on the Army's coastal fortification system, a more precise identification is offered by comparing the preceding technical passage with two unsigned sketches found among the inventor's drawings. The first (Figure 28), illustrating two anchored, buoyant box "torpedoes" depicts internal fuses supplied by electric leads from shore batteries.[103] A closer view of this arrangement is suggested in a second, possibly later drawing, faintly captioned "Submarine Torpedo fired by Electricity or a Galvanic Battery" (Figure 29) more clearly delineating two terminal wires fitted within a globular fuse compartment of a circular or cylindrical mine case, the terminals being fitted with a ruptured filament or possibly pointed carbon poles.[104]

Samuel Colt's characteristic preoccupation with firing his mines precisely beneath the target, as well as a rudimentary grasp of galvanic theory, is evident in the ensuing passage of this revealing effusion:

Now, when an enemy is over the box, and the wires are that instant attached, positive electricity immediately passes along one wire, and negative electricity passes along the

Figure 29.—SECTIONAL PLAN FOR GALVANIC MINE.

other wire, these two kinds of electricity concentrate on the platina wire, instantly heat it red hot, and it fires the gunpowder, and blows the vessel to fragments.[105]

That the author had been present at the Washington demonstration of 20 August is finally apparent in the concluding passage, which not only demonstrates the inventor's sensitivity to professional criticism but also suggests the emotional base for his appeal against further expenditures on coastal fortifications:

Having seen the effects of this wonderful contrivance in the explosion of a stout schooner near Greenleaf's Point, I am as well convinced of its utility for the protection of harbors, and indeed of bays and rivers from the invasion of hostile fleets, as of any other invention which of late has so astonished the world. It has been said that the wires could be raked up by sending boats ahead with rakes and oyster-tongs. I think it would be a rather hazardous business, if not utterly impracticable for the want of a knowledge of the locality of the boxes (for I presume any number of boxes may be sunk in the channel) and with wires; besides the operator or superintendent in one night could sink boxes in the channel in [the] rear of the enemy's ships, which would ensure their destruction, and instead of raking for the wires, you would find the crews taking to their boats and jumping overboard. I trust we may hereafter dispense with our expen-

sive and useless forts on the sea-board. I say *useless*, because they are of no earthly use but to protect the soldiers from the enemy, who can land their men out of gunshot of the fort, and ravage the country, opposed by none but militia. We experienced this last war, in the instance of Forts Detroit, Niagara, Oswego, Castine, and Fort Bowyer.[106]

Although Colt was unprepared at this juncture to provide government officials the ultimate challenge— the destruction of a *moving* vessel within a sizeable field of mines—he nevertheless felt compelled to sustain public awareness of his undersea warfare system. Officers of the American Institute, an early New York association for promotion of the useful arts, provided the restless inventor an irresistible setting for yet another public demonstration in the fall of 1842, importuning both the White House and the Navy Department to permit Colt to demonstrate his Submarine Battery at the Institute's annual fair on Manhattan.[107] To add to Secretary Upshur's mounting disenchantment, Colt rationalized this evident circumvention of professional scrutiny in a note of 12 September to John D. Simms, Chief Clerk of the Navy Department, commenting caustically on his experience at the Washington Navy Yard and asserting:

If I am permitted to conduct my experiments in my own way without being bothered by Navy Yard regulations, I will guarantee to accomplish all that is required of me by Congress at less expense & less time than [I] can otherwise.[108]

Secretary Upshur was by no means satisfied, making it abundantly clear to the American Institute that the Department had no authority to permit a government-supported undertaking to be exploited commercially.[109] On 27 September Upshur bluntly advised Colt that he could honor no further requisitions unless the entrepreneur would henceforth "confer with me as to your course of proceedings." [110]

On the fateful day that Upshur penned this sharp admonition, its recipient sustained a deeply mortifying blow, the conviction of John Colt for murder by a New York court and the announcement immediately thereafter of his death sentence.[111] Secretary Upshur, who chanced to visit the distraught inventor at this juncture, subsequently acceded to Colt's proposal of 6 October that the Submarine Battery be demonstrated at the American Institute fair with the Navy Department's tacit permission.[112] Upshur nevertheless felt obliged to refuse Colt's request for official funds to purchase a target vessel, the 260-ton brig *Volta*, which finally appears to have been acquired with the assistance of the American Institute.[113]

In preparation for his second major New York demonstration, held off Castle Garden on 18 October 1842, Colt acquired an extensive amount of insulated cable, including at least three reels lent by Professor Samuel F. B. Morse, who was concurrently conducting tests of his magnetic telegraph system, in the immediate vicinity, employing copper cabling similarly insulated with tarred thread.[114] Although Colt's own cable-laying preliminaries again attracted little public notice, he secured maximum attention for the actual mining of the *Volta*, offering assurances through the New York *Express* prior to the event that "the galvanic battery will be placed to [at] Castle Garden, so that all who will take the trouble to go into the Garden, which will hold several thousand, can see with ease and distinctness the mode of arranging the wires and of causing the explosion."[115] Thus an estimated forty thousand spectators thronged the Battery and nearby ships on the 18th, including Secretary of War John C. Spencer and, by the inventor's account, "all the Navy and Army officers in port ...," who again took station on the ship-of-the-line *North Carolina*.[116] To his undisguised delight, Colt had yet another surprise for both the press and the assembled officialdom, as he later reported to Upshur:

> Everything on my part was conducted as privately as possible so much so that every reporter for [the New York] newspapers have as yet mistaken even the place where I were stationed when I made the explosion.
>
> The general belief that I would be on board the *North Carolina* with my apparatus crowded her decks to suffocation with every body that could gain admission. Among them of course was many news papers reporters some of which, disappointed in not being able to discover anything of my apparatus have seen fit to reflect upon me for what they deem unnecessary secrecy.[117]

The instantaneous destruction of the *Volta*, signaled by the last salvo of a thirteen-gun salute from the *North Carolina*, deeply moved and indeed mystified the thousands of onlookers congregated at the Battery.

> . . . the great bulk seemed lifted by some unseen power, the bow and stern sunk heavily, and the whole was enveloped by a huge pile of dense mist, some two hundred feet in diameter and about eighty high, through which now and then were seen pieces of timber, of which even the shape could not be guessed.[118]

The mystery that again surrounded Colt's firing arrangements was reflected by Secretary Spencer's unsuccessful effort to discover whether his powder magazine had been anchored beneath the *Volta* or attached directly to her hull. The Washington *Daily* *National Intelligencer* subsequently reported that the *Volta* had been "placed about equidistant between Castle Garden and the *North Carolina* ..., and under it was placed the battery of Mr. Colt, he remaining three-quarters of a mile off, on Governor's Island, ready to apply the electric spark at the concerted signal."[119] In reality, Colt had boarded the Revenue Cutter *Ewing* off the Battery at noon, connecting his firing apparatus with the submerged cable leads and thereafter conducting the experiment from that station, characteristically escaping the attentions of the curious.[120] Evidence is lacking to indicate that the inventor attempted more than a stationary demonstration, notwithstanding the fact that his most recent correspondence with the Navy Department had included rough plans for a channel minefield controlled by two separate observers.[121]

Captain Matthew C. Perry, senior naval observer on board the *North Carolina*, clearly was not impressed. Doubtless recalling the frustration of Robert Fulton's attempts to torpedo the brig *Argus* at New York in 1810, Perry offered the opinion, as reported by the New York *Herald*, that in disbursing the $15,000 allocated for the testing of Colt's Submarine Battery, "one thousand of it should be taken to purchase a vessel, and the balance be divided between one party who volunteer to go aboard the vessel and sail her, and another party who should try to blow her up ...." Considering Colt's frequent and pointed comparisons between the cost of a steam warship and of a major Submarine Battery installation for the defense of New York, it is indeed remarkable that Perry had afforded him considerable assistance for the Castle Garden demonstration.[122]

In concluding his report on the American Institute demonstration, Colt assured Secretary Upshur that "the Gov't is benefited by the information gained by the exhibition,"[123] yet the inventor made no attempt to represent the results as meeting the Congressional requirement of providing "a power sufficient to destroy the largest class of ship, when in motion, passing in or out of harbor."[124] Eighteen months of extensive testing lay ahead before Colt could return to Washington prepared to offer conclusive proof of the practicality of his system of coastal defense.

The final stages in the development of Colt's Submarine Battery were strikingly intertwined with Samuel F. B. Morse's concluding efforts to secure Congressional recognition of his electromagnetic telegraph. Following his demonstration at the American Institute fair, Colt exhibited his galvanic battery at Castle Garden in the same booth from which Morse was attempting to transmit messages to nearby Governor's Island. As reported by the New York *Herald*, Morse experienced difficulties with his transmitter initially: "This would not perform according to the programme, in consequence of the weakness of the Professor's battery. But after the [Submarine Battery] explosion, when it received the accession of Mr. Colt's large battery, it worked very well." [125] Misfortune continued to dog the Professor, however. On the morning of 19 October, Morse arrived for the main demonstration of his invention. After a triumphant initial exchange of signals with his partner, Professor Leonard D. Gale, who was stationed on Governor's Island, Morse was suddenly dismayed to observe his submarine cable innocently hauled up and severed by the crew of a merchantman preparing to get under way (Figure 30). The abrupt termination of this experiment humiliated Morse, who suffered the jeers and insults of uncomprehending onlookers. [126] Undaunted, Morse continued his private experiments at Washington Square, occasionally borrowing cable from Colt and making the discovery late in 1842 that two or more currents could be conducted simultaneously by a single wire, a commercially significant discovery that was eventually designated duplex telegraphy. [127]

Morse's departure for Washington in December and his successful demonstrations on Capitol Hill, culminating in passage of the Telegraph Bill on 3 March 1843, by no means concluded the close association of these embattled inventors. Following Professor Morse's climactic demonstration of 24 May 1844 in the chamber of the Supreme Court, an historic event that followed swiftly upon Colt's final demonstration in Washington, these pioneers of American galvanic technology found themselves indirectly associated in the development of the New York and Offing Magnetic Telegraph Association. This company, which provided notification in Manhattan of ship arrivals off Sandy Hook, was one of the first telegraph enterprises founded by Morse's business associates in 1845 to exploit the commercial feasibility of his magnetic recording telegraph patent. [128]

The shadow of John Colt's approaching execution had hung heavily over further development of the Submarine Battery during the fall of 1842. Its concluding lugubrious events, including the apparent suicide of the convicted and the subsequent flight of

Figure 30.—Submarine telegraph cable. Fabricated by Colt's assistant, Robert Cummings, in a small New York rope walk, this four-stranded submarine cable was employed on 18–19 October 1842 during that inventor's Submarine Battery demonstration and subsequently during Samuel F.B. Morse's telegraph experiment between the Battery and Governor's Island. Considered the first submarine telegraph cable successfully laid in the United States, this lead-sheathed cable—whose individual copper strands were wrapped with cotton yarn impregnated with asphaltum and beeswax— may well have had simpler antecedents in the insulated copper conductors employed by Colt in his experiments at New York and Washington earlier that year.

Cable similar to that illustrated was successfully employed by Colt in the construction of the New York and Offing telegraph line from Manhattan to Coney Island and Fire Island in 1846, which he completed in partnership with the associates of Samuel F. B. Morse.

his widow to Europe, clearly preoccupied the distraught younger Colt for several months. [129] Early in 1843, however, the entrepreneur resumed his remark-

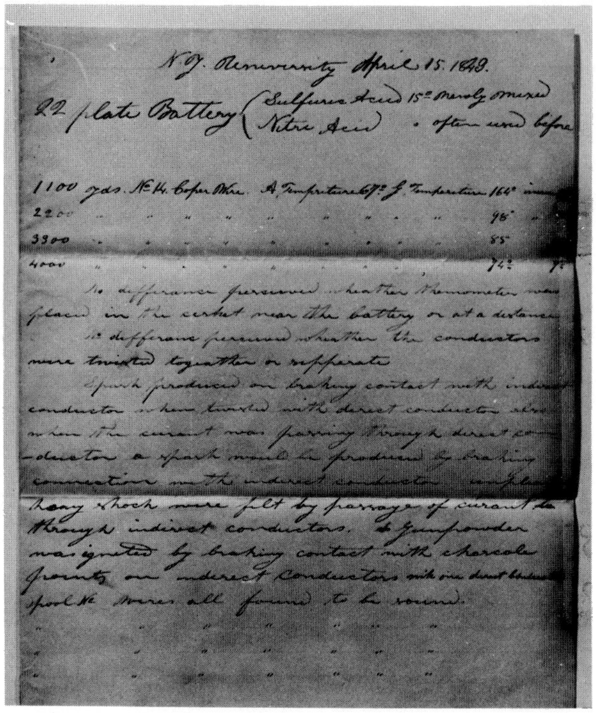

N.Y. University April 15, 1843.

22 plate Battery	{	Sulfuric Acid	15º	Newly Mixed
	{	Nitre Acid	"	often used before

1100 yds. Nº 14. Coper Wire.	A, Temperature 67º.	G, Temperature	164º	increase	97º
2200 "	" " " " "	" " "	98°	"	31
3300 "	" " " " "	" " "	85	"	18
4000 "	" " " " "	" " "	74º	"	7º

No differance persieved wheather thermometer was placed in the cirket [circuit] near the battery or at a distance

No differanc percieved wheather the conductors were twisted togeather or sepperate

Spark produced on braking contact with indirect conductor when twisted with direct conductor also when the curant was passing through direct conductor a spark would be produced by braking connection with indirect conductor unpleasantly heavy shock were felt by passage of curant through indirect conductors. Gunpowder was ignited by braking contact with charcole points on indirect conductors with one direct conductor

Spool Nº   wires all found to be sound.

    "   "   "   "   "   "   "

    "   "   "   "   "   "   "

    "   "   "   "   "   "   "

Figure 31.—COLT'S EXPERIMENT ON THE HEATING EFFECT OF ELECTRICITY ON COPPER LEADS OF VARYING LENGTH, 15 APRIL 1843 (with transcription). Conducted at Washington Square, this materials test reveals Colt's inquisitive bent and indicates that he was then considering a carbon arc fuse as an alternative to the platinum filament detonator.

ably deliberate task of refining the various elements of his mine warfare system, acquiring a fresh supply of gunpowder from the New York Navy Yard and ordering additional rolled copper wire and platinum filament from Brown and Elton.[130] From February through April, Colt carried out a series of experiments to determine the relative heating effects of electricity on copper and platinum wire (Figure 31).[131] From tests on platinum filament of varying diameter conducted at New York University on 23 March, the inventor concluded: "Inferance from experiments are that it is necessary to have but one exploding power (platinum wire) at the point of explosion. Wire should be coiled in small diameters & as close together as possible without touching." [132] Such materials tests and experiments, while necessary for practical implementation of the Submarine Battery system, did not represent the unique core of that conception. In the final professional judgment on Colt's scheme rendered in 1844, it was conjectured that the inventor had based his claims to originality mainly on an application of the galvanic process to the ignition of gunpowder. In

reality, Colt had publically disclaimed any such basis for originality as early as 11 May 1843, when the *Army and Navy Chronicle and Scientific Repository* published a succinct letter on galvanic rock blasting that he had posted from Washington Square a week earlier. Adverting to recent articles in that journal regarding the use of electricity for rock blasting by British engineers, Colt pointed out:

The first person who made any practical use of electricity for the purpose of igniting large masses of gunpowder was Mr. Moses Shaw, of Boston, Mass. His experiments were made as early as the year 1828. He applied it for the purpose of blasting rocks. An account of his method was communicated to Professor Silliman by the late Dr. Chilton, of this city; and it was published in the American Journal of Science and Arts, vol. xvi, 1829. Mr. Shaw at first made use of the ordinary electrical machine; but, finding it inconvenient in damp weather, he, by recommendation of Dr. Hare, of Philadelphia, employed the *calarimater* [calorimotor], a form of galvanic battery constructed by Dr. H., in which the plates are so connected together as to act as one pair. Its power of igniting in all weather would extend a distance sufficient to blast rocks with safety. An account of his experiments was published by Dr. Hare in the American Journal of

Science and Arts, vol. xxi 1831, and again with additions, in vol. xxvi 1834; in which latter article Dr. Hare recommends a battery of a number of galvanic plates. Since that time, both common and galvanic electricity have been usefully employed by various persons in many parts of *this country*, for the purpose of igniting magazines of gunpowder, and for years before the *English engineers* attempted to break up the *Royal George*. Electricity for blasting was employed at *Harlem, Sing Sing, Black Rock, Lockport, Buffalo, and other places*, with perfect success. *In one instance, at Black Rock, no less than thirty blasts were fired at one time, by only one battery*.[133]

Although containing no direct reference to the Submarine Battery, Colt's public note, coming well after his first three mining demonstrations, left little doubt, for those who chose to read it, as to the galvanic character of his system. During the spring and summer of 1843, a period that saw further development of his tinfoil cartridge venture, Colt advertised from Norfolk to Portland for a suitable target vessel, ultimately selecting an 81-foot barque, the *Brunette*, which he discovered at Woods Hole.[134] Tests of various combinations of batteries and multistranded cable occupied the inventor during the fall of 1843; by the following February, Colt had developed an eleven-plate battery designed to supply his projected minefield through nine-stranded copper conductors.[135]

Climax at Washington

As experiments, these, as many others have been, were very beautiful and striking; but in the practical application of this apparatus to purposes of war, we have no confidence.

Army and Navy Chronicle and Scientific
Repository, WASHINGTON, 18 APRIL 1844

Colt had meanwhile made arrangements for a final conclusive demonstration of his Submarine Battery at Washington (Figure 32) early in the first session of the twenty-eighth Congress. The inventor was doubtless encouraged by the progress of the Morse telegraph system and possibly also impelled by accounts of the armored floating battery currently under construction at Hoboken by Robert L. Stevens for the defense of New York.[136] Late in November 1843, Colt had dispatched the *Brunette to* Alexandria, where she was temporarily docked by Stephen Shinn, his shipping agent. The magnitude of the forthcoming demonstration first became apparent on 16 December when Shinn reported the arrival from the naval magazine

Figure 33.—THE *Princeton* DISASTER, 28 FEBRUARY 1844. President John Tyler, who had witnessed the first demonstration of Colt's Submarine Battery at Washington in 1842, observed the first two test firings of Captain Robert F. Stockton's flawed 12-inch "Peacemaker" on board the *Princeton* before the fatal salvo was fired.

Figure 32.—"THE LAST EXPERIMENT OF MR. COLT'S SUBMARINE BATTERY IN WASHINGTON CITY" 1844. Such is the description of this oil painting by the artist, A^n. Gibert, contained in his receipt for $60.00 for this work, addressed to Samuel Colt from New York on 15 October 1844. The locale of Gibert's painting had long been believed to be New York harbor. Close comparison of this painting with an unsigned sketch in the Colt Papers, however, reveals not only a general similarity of perspective but numerous common elements in the background, including the shiphouse and other buildings of the Navy Yard and the prominent old eight-story sugar refinery, located near the eastern entrance of the Washington Canal. Evidence is presently lacking as to whether Gibert witnessed the last Washington demonstrations. Gibert may have worked from the anonymous sketch (Figure 36) certified by Colt as factually "correct".

on Ellis Island of 150 barrels of gunpowder, a dangerous consignment that Shinn prudently stored ashore in a local magazine.[137] The precaution proved fortuitous, for on 28 February, shortly before Colt and his assistant, Robert Cummings, returned to Washington, the capital was deeply shocked by the *Princeton* disaster (Figure 33), an ordnance demonstration accident that occurred on board the new steam frigate *Princeton* while she was cruising with President Tyler and his entourage on the Potomac near Mount Vernon. That tragedy, from which the President narrowly escaped, claimed the lives of five members of the Presidential party, including the newly appointed Secretary of State Abel P. Upshur and Secretary of the Navy Thomas W. Gilmer, greatly hastening the revolution in naval ordnance design. Ironically, this disaster scarcely raised questions regarding the immediate presence of Cabinet members at such potentially dangerous demonstrations. In Upshur's death, significantly, the administration lost its only member intimately familiar with the secret of Colt's Submarine Battery.[138]

Such was the somber background for Colt's request on 11 March to Acting Secretary of the Navy, Commodore Lewis Warrington, for assistance in completing arrangements for his own mining demonstration. In accordance with a Senate resolution introduced by John J. Crittenden on 19 March, Colt was provided with anchors, boats, timber, and mooring line from the Washington Navy Yard, as well as a chart of the Potomac and Eastern Branch rivers above Alexandria (Figure 34).[139] Gratified by this official assistance, Colt worked rapidly with Cummings in deploying his minefield and on 1 April reported to Representative Henry A. Wise that "I have fortified the river leding to the Navy Yard & the ship is to be got under way with all her sails set & blown up while at her greatest speed."[140] Subsequent announcements to the press on 1 April, pointedly emphasizing the experiment's danger to imprudently curious parties of boaters, left little doubt that Samuel Colt intended to satisfy Congressional requirements for his Submarine Battery performance beyond the margin of reasonable doubt.[141]

The entrepreneur's sense of timing could scarcely be faulted. Early in April 1844, the National Institute for the Promotion of Science convened the first major literary and scientific convention held in the United States, a week-long meeting of leading scientists that was opened at the Treasury Department under the personal sponsorship of President Tyler and members of his cabinet. Attended by numerous members of Congress and the diplomatic corps, this remarkable convocation represented a major effort by advocates of the National Institute to secure its designation as recipient of James Smithson's bequest. Incidentally, it provided an attractive occasion for inventors, notably including both Morse and Colt, to draw attention to their current undertakings.[142]

Much more dramatic matters were at hand in the capital, however. By the spring of 1844, Congress found itself intensely preoccupied with the proposed annexation of Texas, an issue that had been revived by President Tyler, partly with the approaching presidential campaign in view. Fundamentally, however, the Administration was responding to mounting diplomatic pressure from the young Republic of Texas that presented Washington with the risky alternatives of offering the Lone Star Republic early admission to the Union or witnessing its independent national development, possibly accompanied by the abolition of slavery in the Southwest, doubtless with British economic and political encouragement. The military implications of yet another confrontation with Britain

thus were already taking disturbing form when Colt began his final overtures in Washington.[143]

Congressional nerves, which had been distinctly set on edge by the *Princeton* tragedy, had inadvertently been further frayed by a quixotic incident on 11 March when Major Samuel Ringgold's celebrated "Flying Artillery"—established in 1838 as the first company of horse artillery in the U.S. Army—conducted a thunderous demonstration on Capitol Hill, in imprudent proximity to the East Front, bringing this *corps d'élite* to Congressional attention in a manner not anticipated: "The first firing made sad havoc with the window glass in the Capitol . . . . All the glass in the Supreme Court room was knocked into pi[eces] while the court was in session. Many of the Senate committee rooms fared as badly, and nearly all the glass of the Senate Chamber." [144] The Senate, though by no means amused, managed, as revealed in *The Congressional Globe,* to retain its aplomb in proceeding to an unexpected adjournment:

Mr. [John T.] Morehead here remarked that the hour for the orders of the day had nearly arrived; but several Senators had assured him that they would be compelled to leave their seats in consequence of the exposed situation of the Chamber—almost all the glass in the windows having been broken by the firing of the United States artillery. If it would, therefore, be agreeable to the Senator from Pennsylvania [Mr. Buchanan] who was entitled to the floor on the Oregon question, he would move that the Senate adjourn.[145]

Curiously, a similar motion was offered by Representative Alexander Duncan one month later, on 12 April, the day before Colt's announced Submarine Battery demonstration, with somewhat more chaotic result as reported, tongue in cheek, by the *Alexandria Gazette:*

Mr. Duncan at last took the floor, and said something about blowing up.

But no man seemed to understand the precise nature of the explosion at hand. Some members stated that Mr. Colt was to blow up the Potomac: others that he was about to blow up the Department of State, including Oregon and Texas; and others again broached the strange idea that the company of light artillery, which on a former day had made some experiments on the window-frames of the Chambers of the Senate and Supreme Court, was about to subject the Capitol to further tests of its strength.[146]

During heated debate that ensued in the House, Representative John B. Thompson sagely urged that an early adjournment might enable the members to observe final preparations for Colt's experiment.[147] Subsequent press accounts of the Submarine Battery demonstration, the more florid of which appear to

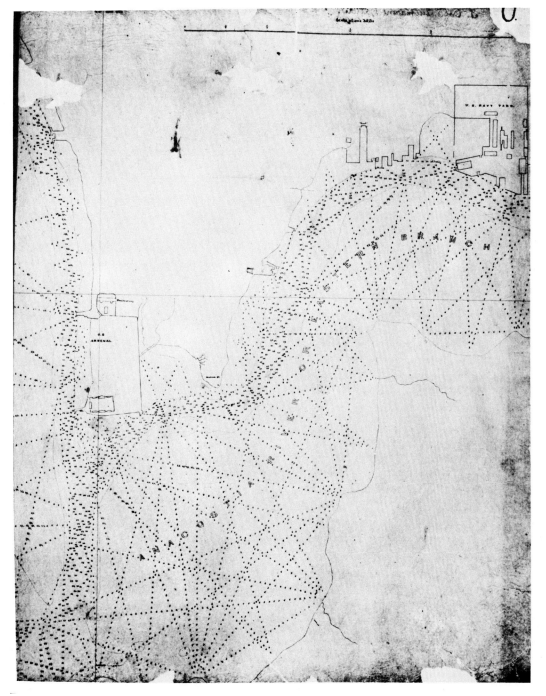

Figure 34.—CHART OF THE EASTERN BRANCH OR ANACOS-
TIA RIVER. This portion of a larger chart of the Potomac
and Eastern Branch between Alexandria and the Long
Bridge provides the locale of Samuel Colt's Washington
demonstrations of 1842 and 1844. Found among his patent
drawings for the Submarine Battery, it bears several lightly
penciled sighting lines across the vicinity of his minefield in
the Navy Yard approaches of the Eastern Branch. Such
sighting lines accord well with the principle involved in his
two-observer system, as these partially erased lines intersect
across eight faintly marked buoys laid in two lines of four
each athwart the channel. Colt could have achieved the
effect of a two-observer system by having the *Styx* piloted
directly through this minefield (employing some landmark
near the Navy Yard), while positioning himself at right
angles, either on Poplar Point or on the north shore of the
Eastern Branch. Partial erasure of these sighting lines, as
well as the absence of mines actually detonated, raises doubt
regarding this apparent arrangement.

have been inspired and perhaps edited by the inventor, suggest however that Colt had deliberately completed his preparations sufficiently in advance to frustrate comprehensive evaluation by either federal officials or Washington newsmen.[148]

The scene of Colt's climactic demonstration on 13 April 1844, that broad reach of the Eastern Branch extending from the Arsenal on Greenleaf Point to the venerable shiphouses of the Navy Yard, had been widely advertised:

> . . . the whole populace was in a fidget of satisfaction and impatience—everybody in every place, from the halls of Congress and the Executive Departments down to the boarding house kitchen and boot-blacks' cellars, were hurrying through the business of the morning to ensure an early dinner and a sight of *the blow up*.[149]

Owing yet again to the absence of official supervision of Colt's experiments, no report by military professionals survives to establish the precise preparation of the inventor's first major minefield (Figure 35), the location of his observation post, or the sequence of events surrounding the destruction of the *Brunette,* which had been rechristened *Styx* for her final cruise. Fortunately, however, a chart, signal schedules, contemporary newspaper accounts, and a surviving on-the-spot sketch provide substantial insight into the events of the Washington Navy Yard test.

The intended scenario of Colt's demonstration was outlined in two brief schedules drafted by Lieutenant Junius Boyle of the Navy Yard, who had volunteered to conn the target vessel to the minefield's immediate vicinity. It was agreed that about 4:30 in the afternoon the inventor would signify his readiness by "a small explosion" (possibly a pistol shot), following which Boyle would respond from the *Styx* by lowering her topsail three times. After removing the national ensign, Boyle and his small crew were to leave the target vessel in a boat and, when clear of danger, fire a rocket. Boyle also provided Colt a minuted schedule of gun signals from the Navy Yard that, while outlining the intended sequence of events, contains no indication that a second observer may have assisted the inventor from some vantage point within the Yard:

Signals between Mr. Colt and the Navy Yard.

On the arrival of the Secretary a Salute of 17 guns will be fired and the Ensign hoisted to the Sheers.

At 5 PM a gun will be fired which will be followed by an explosion from Mr. Colt's battery.

At 5.10 another gun will be fired when the wreck will be removed from the channel by an explosion.

At 5.20 another gun will be fired when several simultanius explosions will take place.

At 5.30 another gun will be fired when a final explosion will conclude the experiments.

Junius Boyle [150]

Here one finds no evidence that the signals were to be integrated with a two-observer arrangement: no evidence that Colt would have been advised by sound signals that the *Styx* was passing through successive ranges of mines sighted from a second observation post. As soon became apparent, this scenario did not materialize precisely as planned.

A vivid account of the actual demonstration was provided by one "Sigma," a reporter of the Washington *Daily National Intelligencer,* on whom the inventor appears to have made a favorable impression.

> I strolled down to the shores of the Eastern Branch about three o'clock; yet though it was more than an hour before the appointed time, I found thousands there before me, patiently waiting (under no very merciful sun, either) the destined hour to arrive. Stationing myself on an elevated bluff, I enjoyed, in delighted silence, the panorama which surrounded me. The undulating shores on the opposite bank of the river, with their woods and farm houses, and cultivated fields; on the left, the navy yard, with its ship-houses and workshops; on the right, the arsenal, with Giesbury point and Alexandria in the distance; close by, the wharves and river beach, covered with people; the nearer heights covered with carriages and vehicles of every description, with riders on horseback, companies of children, and anxious mothers trying to restrain them from venturing to the precipices; while below, the placid blue stream, gently rippled by a very light breeze, and glittering in the rays of a fervid, unclouded sun, covered with boats of all sizes, rowing or sailing to and fro—these objects combined in one wide *coup d'oeil,* presented a scene which, for variety, interest and picturesque beauty, could scarcely be surpassed.
>
> In the middle of the stream, and in full view, lay the object on which all eyes were fastened—a ship of about five hundred tons, very old, but newly painted, black with a white streak, her sails much patched and weather beaten, having at her mainmast head a red flag, and at the mizzen mast the American ensign floating beautifully in the breeze. She was at anchor, and near her were boats that seemed, from their motions, to be in communication with those on board. Presently a steamboat heaved in view and, taking her station at a convenient distance, began to let off steam; and before long, another and longer appeared, having her deck black with a crowd of people and bearing the national colors, having as it was understood, the President on board, accompanied by the Heads of Departments and other offices of Government.
>
> As all were now waiting with much impatience, a gun was heard from the navy yard, which was followed by others, till

Figure 35.—CONCEPTUAL CROSS-SECTION OF AN OBSERVA-
TION MINEFIELD FOR COLT'S REFLECTED SUBMARINE BAT-
TERY.   This section from the 13-foot watercolor of Colt's
matured Submarine Battery scheme indicates that individual
sighting lines from the "torpedo tower" would fall on the
water surface directly above clusters of submerged, buoyant
mines. Linked horizontally in clusters of five cases (cf. Figures 28 and 29), these globular mines appear to be served
in cluster by a single insulated lead from the main transmission cable running across the river or harbor bottom,
suggesting that a target vessel would receive the impact of
five simultaneous explosions.

a salute of seventeen guns was fired. We now began to hope
that the play had begun. Every eye was turned towards the
ship; but she did not move. A little boat advanced and
removed certain buoys which had been floating near the
spot where the battery lay; and soon after a low and peculiar
sound was heard, when a most beautiful jet, of mingled
water, fire and smoke, rose to a considerable height near the
opposite shore, and as the water fell back in white translucent
masses, the smoke, colored by the sun's rays with all the dyes
of the prism, slowly melted into the air, while the grains
of wet powder, ignited and smoking, fell in soft showers upon
the bright surface of the river. This exhibition rose as if by
the touch of magic, and seemed intended as a sort of prelude
to convince the waiting multitude that there was a prospect
of being paid for their walk.[151]

The observant reporter, who had referred to Colt
in his opening paragraph as "this new Fulton,"
regrettably offered no comment on the inventor's
preparations or the location of his firing station during the demonstration. An equally effusive colleague,
who styled himself "Peter Primrose," subsequently
reported that "a poplar grove on a point of land
upon the opposite shore, and nearly abreast of the
ship, was pointed out to us as the spot where Mr. Colt
was posted with his apparatus." [152] Poplar Point lay
at the southerly end of two cross-channel lines partly
erased from Colt's chart of the Eastern Branch.

Figure 36.—Destruction of the barque *Styx* by Colt's Submarine Battery off the Washington Navy Yard, 13 April 1844. This unsigned contemporary sketch of the climactic demonstration for Congress is annotated as "correct," evidently by the inventor.

Regardless of his exact location overlooking the minefield, he had succeeded once again in evading scrutiny by scientifically astute observers and the public at large. During the ensuing moments of his demonstration, however, he was to be embarrassed somewhat by several waterborne observers.

At length the American ensign was lowered, and the few persons on board the ship [*Styx*], passing over her side, were rowed off, amid the huzzas which rose from the shores, and the vessel, abandoned to the breeze, commenced her fateful voyage. She proceeded slowly, and as steadily as if navigated by the most skilful crew. As she approached the spot where the buoys had floated, an explosion took place, and the water was thrown up in a pyramid, but a few yards ahead of her. "Ah!" exclaimed a thousand tongues, "what a pity! it was a failure after all!" The ship held on her course, and in a few minutes another mountain of water, larger and blacker than the first, rose on her larboard bow, and so close to her that she rocked under the undulation. "Oh, he has missed her! but it was very near." The words were scarcely uttered when a third explosion took place—the bows and bowsprit of the ship, instantly shattered to atoms, were thrown into the air. The fore part of the vessel was lifted up almost out of the water, and then immediately sank, while the stern continued above water, and the mizzenmast was left still standing, though in an inclined position. The spars and sails hung in

confusion, being suddenly blackened by the smoke, and the whole presenting a wreck in the highest degree picturesque—in fact a study for the pencil [Figure 36]. A momentary pause of gratified suspense took place, and then the shores resounded with heartfelt plaudits, subsiding into long-continuing murmurs of admiration. The gratification was unbounded. Nothing could have been more completely successful. There was no accident, no injury, no disappointment in any respect; the public expectation was not only met but surpassed; and when the boat containing the crew darted swiftly to the wreck, and with some difficulty restored the stripes and stars to their former station, it required no stretch of the imagination to fancy that we beheld a captive invader, which had been compelled to strike, and was now taken possession of as lawful prize.[153]

The contrast with the *Princeton* disaster was evident; yet, as sensed by another reporter, the experiment did not come off exactly as scheduled: "It would seem that the explosion was made a little too soon, as, had the battery struck the vessel a minute later, she would have been completely destroyed,"[154] In his cryptic report to the Navy Department on 22 April, Colt indicated two factors that had complicated his task: "The number of small boats upon the river, which from the position I occupied could not be distinguished from pieces of the wreck,

Figure 37.—WASHINGTON IN 1834, AS VIEWED FROM BEYOND THE NAVY YARD. This pastoral vista suggests that a relatively unobstructed view was available from the Anacostia heights, approximately one mile south of Colt's minefield, which was sown on the lower reaches of the Eastern Branch, between Greenleaf Point (extreme left) and Poplar Point. Opposite low-lying Poplar Point rises an eight-storied sugar refinery; to the east are seen the Washington Navy Yard's sawmill and shiphouse, while to the west, on Greenleaf Point, is visible the wall-enclosed complex of the Washington Arsenal.

deterred me from proceeding further after the destruction of the vessel, for fear of accident."[155]

The location and character of Colt's observation post, elements that were critical to a professional evaluation of his mine warfare system, still remain obscure and indeed constitute principal elements of the enigma that yet surround his Submarine Battery demonstrations. In reporting to Secretary of the Navy John Y. Mason, he asserted that his "position in this case . . . was on the opposite bank of the river something more than two miles distant from the ship." [156] Here again the inventor alluded to no second ob-server. Colt may indeed have conducted his demonstration from an overlook on the Anacostia heights, but a reconnaisance of that area indicates that he could have secured no effective view of the mined area from the distance he alleged. Even from a closer overlook, as suggested in Figure 37 (or by a modern view from the Frederick Douglass home on Cedar Hill), Colt would not have enjoyed the various angles of reflection necessary for precise target positioning that was embodied in his single observer system.

That Colt considered utilizing posts within half a mile of his minefield is suggested by sighting lines

Figure 38.—THE HEART OF THE ENIGMA. This enlarged portion of Gibert's painting illustrating the destruction of the *Styx* focuses on three locations that may have been involved in Colt's successful mining of that vessel: the sawmill and shiphouse of the Washington Navy Yard and an abandoned eight-story sugar refinery. Originally constructed in 1798, the sugar refinery was later utilized as a brewery, clearly the highest potential command post immediately adjacent to Colt's minefield. The log of the U.S.S. *Union,* which has been identified as the steamer then refitting at the Navy Yard sawmill, sheds no light on these proceedings.

partially erased from his chart (see Figure 34), that terminate in box-shaped positions marked on both Poplar Point and the north bank of the Eastern Branch, suggesting his use of a simplified "torpedo tower." Mindful of his observation post's vulnerability to naval gunfire, the inventor emphasized its remote location, doubtless to confound his professional critics. On 3 June Colt wrote to Representative Henry C. Murphy of the House Committee on Naval Affairs, asserting that "a fisherman's house, or barn, or even the top of a tree, any where within five miles distance could be made the position from which the engineer could operate on the enemy" [157] (Figure 37). Such assurances, which square badly with Colt's patent drawings, effectively masked his actual firing arrangements at Washington, while revealing anew his constant concern for avoiding reference to that most unique element of his proposed system—the "torpedo tower."

Herein lies the ultimate element of the enigma

surrounding Colt's final demonstrations, on which the subsequent inventories of his equipment shed no positive light. The inventor's papers contain no evidence that he employed either a reflecting mirror or a control grid in accomplishing the destruction of the *Styx.* Far more useful than a distant farmhouse would have been the abandoned eight-story sugar refinery (Figure 38) that figures prominently in both contemporary depictions of the Navy Yard experiment. That structure would have afforded a superb overlook of the mined channel, with the requisite range of angles of reflection for his rows of mines, while fully concealing the operator from the throng.[158] Colt's guarded statements, including his reference to "the engineer" in his hypothetical example, suggest that he had employed and indeed personally operated some form of a single observer system in detonating select mines laid athwart the Navy Yard channel.

The significance of the Submarine Battery's climactic demonstration was assiduously driven home for Congress by two noticeably sympathetic press observers, most strikingly by the aforementioned "Sigma," who concluded:

> May this important invention, now brought to the test of experiment, and proved to be so eminently successful, prove the happy means of forever preventing the approach of an invader to shores thus guarded and rendered impregnable by the force of American science and enterprise; and may lasting honor and merited reward crown the inventor of so great a public benefit! Twenty-four hours are sufficient completely to protect the entrance of any harbor in the Union, for no foe, unless bereft of reason, will run into the jaws of so certain and so speedy a destruction.[159]

Military professionals, denied the opportunity to monitor Colt's difficult undertaking closely, took a decidedly more skeptical view of the Navy Yard demonstration, an attitude well reflected in the *Army and Navy Chronicle and Scientific Repository,* which concluded its brief notice: "As experiments, these, as many others have been, were very beautiful and striking, but in the practical application of this apparatus to purposes of war, we have no confidence." [160] Officials at the Washington Navy Yard had particular reason to regret the destruction of the *Styx* off Poplar Point, for her wreck, not fully disintegrated by a subsequent demolition effort and mine-firing demonstration carried out by Colt on 20 April [161] continued to obstruct the narrow approach channel and gradually built up a major sandbar that embarrassed ship movements in and out of the Yard virtually to the eve of the Civil War. [162]

Judgment

Mr. Colt may, perhaps, not attempt to found his claims to originality on the invention of the galvanic process, to which he can have no title, but on a new application of this process to a method of harbor defence; and also on a new arrangement of subaqueous magazines for the same purpose.

JOSEPH HENRY TO SECRETARY OF WAR
WILLIAM WILKINS, 3 MAY 1844

Samuel Colt's final lobbying efforts in behalf of his Submarine Battery—although favored somewhat by current Congressional anxiety regarding Great Britain's reaction to the Texas annexation treaty submitted to the Senate on 22 April 1844 by President Tyler —were destined to be vitiated by widespread official dissatisfaction with the highly secretive, yet superficially public, manner in which his invention had been demonstrated. The imminent approach of the Presidential campaign, beginning with nominating conventions scheduled at Baltimore late in May, had already become a major preoccupation in Washington.[163] Thus on 19 April, three days after Colt submitted a memorial to Congress requesting consideration of his "great expenditure of time and money" in perfecting the Submarine Battery, Representative James J. McKay, Chairman of the House Ways and Means Committee, introduced a resolution that deeply disquieted the inventor. McKay's motion directed the Secretaries of War and Navy to report to that House, "whether the combustible agent used by Mr. Colt was a secret before he made the same known at the seat of Government; and whether the mode of its application to harbor defence be new; and if new, what objections there are against its adoption, if objections do exist." [164] It may well be noted that this sharply interrogatory motion, which was promptly agreed to by the House, was followed immediately and perhaps pointedly that day by a report from the Secretary of War regarding *official* tests of the strength and utility of wrought iron cannon.[165] Shocked by the McKay Resolution, which effectively wrested the initiative from advocates of the Submarine Battery, Colt hastily wrote to William Gibbs McNeill on 22

April, urging him to journey to Washington immediately to aid him in securing a *quid pro quo* for his long sustained efforts:

Movements are making to kill me of[f] without ceremony. A resolution was offered the other day in the House of Representatives. I presume at the instance of some officers of the Army hostile to my new mode of fortification, calling on the Secretarys of War & of the Navy for information as to the plans of my invention[,] the claims which I have if any to origonality &c, &c. The Navy department I think will treat the subject fairly but the Sec'y of War has refered the resolution to the Ordnance Department & the Engenear beauroughs, people of all others the least calculated to give a just repoart in a matter directly hostile to their own profession. Col Tolcot [George Talcott] & in fact nearly every officer of the ordnance department has been hostile to every invention I ever made & I can't hope for any other result in my present cace.

In these outraged passages, Colt clearly revealed his profound distrust of those professionals on whose judgment the fate of his Submarine Battery inevitably rested. In his desperation, the frustrated inventor advanced one final argument:

Neither the ordnance or ingineer Departments have a right to report on this matter for they have no knowledge of my plans of fortification & under the secret arrangements between me and the late Sec'y of the Navy they never can be inlitined on the subject without my permission.[166]

After attempting to enlist McNeill's influence in persuading the Engineer and Ordnance bureaus to submit simple disclaimers of knowledge of his Submarine Battery to the Secretary of War, Colt wrote on 24 April to the recently appointed Secretary of the Navy, John Y. Mason, providing a summary review of his several experiments and driving home the contention that

47

in no single instance have I failed in the use of my submarine battery, and that the combined results of my experiments proved beyond all doubt that it can be successfully employed with the most perfect ease and safety to destroy the largest class of ships of war when in motion passing in or out of harbour without the necessity of approach within reach of shot from guns of the largest calibre.[167]

Secretary Mason, who had assumed his duties on 26 March, had neither attended the Washington Navy Yard demonstration nor attempted to discover the secret of the Colt system vouchsafed to the ill-fated Upshur. In the absence of professional evaluations of the Washington Navy Yard or preceding demonstrations of the Submarine Battery, Mason considered himself in no position to support the inventor's evident expectation of a substantial final honorarium from Congress. The Secretary's dilemma was perhaps most concretely aggravated by the doubtful credibility of Colt's statement on 22 April regarding the actual distance of his observation post from the *Styx* at the time of her destruction off the Navy Yard.[168]

Under these circumstances, Secretary Mason cooly moved to conclude the Navy Department's role, securing from Colt on 25 April an initial statement of his expenses that included his draughts for materials and services totaling $21,867.71 during the preceding two years of experimentation. To this account, Colt added the observation that the figures did not include his travel expenses, a discrete overture to the question of a Congressional honorarium.[169] While appreciative of Colt's expectations, Secretary Mason found no substantial technical data on the Submarine Battery and its performance in the inventor's final appeal on 1 May to the Navy Department. Instead, Colt had enclosed for historical perspective a copy of the contract concluded with Robert Fulton by William Pitt the Younger in 1804, reserving to Great Britain exclusive benefit of that American inventor's plans "for attacking fleets by submarine bombs." [170]

The British government had indeed ultimately not rewarded the peripatetic Fulton for his considerable mining efforts, and Samuel Colt was destined to receive no final award from Congress for the successful demonstration of his Submarine Battery. While the Navy Department attempted to close the account of Colt's expenses, Secretary of War William Wilkins sought authoritative answers to those questions raised by the McKay Resolution regarding the novelty of Colt's "combustible agent." [171] Unknown to the scientists and military professionals subsequently queried by Wilkins (Appendix 5), the much publicized "secret

of Colt's Submarine Battery," insofar as it represented a new contribution to undersea warfare, did not actually reside in his mine's galvanic firing device but in its unique and not yet wholly proven single observer system for gauging the proper moment of detonation. Initially, Wilkins sought and found himself unable to obtain information from Colt himself on any technical aspect of the Submarine Battery. The inventor, who had attempted unsuccessfully to visit Wilkins on 20 April, subsequently wrote to the Secretary requesting him to confirm

that no communication has ever been received at your Department from me, on the subject of my new mode of fortification; and that you possessed no further information on the subject, than the natural inferances framed from witnessing his [my] public exhibitions of its effects....

The relations existing between me and the Government on this subject, are such, that neither the Government or myself have a right to make any of my plans known to the public, and as a communication from either your ordnance or ingineer bureaus must inevitably be breaking the good faith of the Government towards me in case they should give any hints which must lead to an exposure of any of my plans, I am compelled to enter this my most solemn protest against anything being said or reported by your Department, except the simple fact that *nothing whatever is known to you of the matter* [Colt's emphasis].[172]

In replying to this peremptory message on 7 May, Wilkins confessed being "discouraged by the terms of your letter," but renewed his offer to receive any explanations "tending to elucidate your proposed scheme of harbor defence, or your claim to originality of invention. [173] Having no intention of divulging his secret in this fashion, Colt responded with the assertion that

I have already made full explanations to the Navy Department upon the subject, which are deposited in its secret archives. To communicate these to another Department would, I conceive, not only be unnecessary, but greatly increase the risk of making public matters which it is essential should be kept secret. Should the Navy Department desire any further information, I shall hold myself in readiness at all times to furnish what may be necessary to enable the head of that Department to understand the efficiency and value of my invention.[174]

As revealed in the subsequent publication of this epistolary duel, Secretary Mason reported to Wilkins on 7 May that, notwithstanding indications that Colt had divulged the details of his Submarine Battery to Secretary Upshur in 1841 under the injunction of secrecy, "there is nothing in existence in this [Navy] department to show, so far as I am informed, that the secret had been divulged by him, or is applicable to the purposes of the government, without some arrangement with Mr. Colt, which this department has no authority to make." [175] With this additionally discouraging information on hand, Secretary Wilkins was in no mood to countenance Colt's final request on 9 May that he be permitted to examine a copy of the report being drafted by the War Department for submission to the House of Representatives. An arrangement, clearly implied in Colt's wish to make suggestions regarding "the existing relations between the United States government and myself," was not destined to be concluded. [176]

During the preceding week, Secretary Wilkins had received advisory opinions that confirmed his impression that Colt's Submarine Battery, while possibly containing novel elements, relied primarily on galvanic arrangements known to scientists for more than a decade. On 1 May, Professor Robert Hare, distinguished professor of chemistry at the University of Pennsylvania, submitted a documented review of his own and other experiments: ". . . as respects the employment of a galvanic current to ignite a wire, and by means thereof to explode gunpowder, whether for the purpose of rock-blasting, or for warlike defence or annoyance, the galvanic process employed by Mr. Colt has not the slightest claims to originality." [177] Recalling his own experiments as early as 1820 involving the galvanic ignition of gaseous mixtures, as well as his subsequent association with Moses Shaw in the development of galvanic rock blasting, Hare drew attention to subsequent applications of this method to submarine demolitions in Great Britain, France, and India between 1839 and 1841, most notably demonstrated in the demolition of the *Royal George* wreck. Recognizing Colt's ingenuity and good judgment in availing himself of this galvanic arrangement, Hare was, nevertheless, perplexed by the "great difficulty of conceiving how it can be applied so as to avail against movable bodies like ships of war. If Mr. Colt can so employ an exploding apparatus as to defend a harbor, I can see no objection to the project, except that it must be very precarious." [178] Unwittingly, in referring to the problem of how to mine moving hostile vessels, the Philadelphian had identified Samuel Colt's most unique theoretical contribution to the evolution of undersea warfare technology.

No less impressive than the judgment of Robert Hare was the opinion offered to the War Department on 3 May by Professor Joseph Henry (Appendix 8),

the distinguished galvanic physicist at Princeton (Figure 39). Destined to be called to Washington in 1846 as the first Secretary of the Smithsonian Institution, Henry had achieved international recognition in 1831–32 by virtue of his publications on electromagnetic induction, which laid the basis for the electromagnetic telegraph and numerous industrial applications. Frequently in correspondence with Samuel F. B. Morse, Professor Henry had on occasion borrowed insulated cable from that inventor for his own experiments and had given him strong encouragement in perfecting his telegraph at a critical point in his career. For his part, Professor Morse proved no less considerate of a fellow inventor. Quite evidently alerted by the apprehensive Colt as to Henry's new advisory responsibility, Morse wrote to that distinguished scientist on 30 April 1844, advising rather pointedly that "I informed him [Colt] that you would speak your mind prudently and without fear or favor [and] that he need not apprehend anything adverse from you, as I presumed [that] all you would testify in regard to the mode he adopted would be that he had not imparted any knowledge of it to you, and therefore nothing could be said respecting it, but that a method could be devised for accomplishing what he accomplished on known scientific principles." [179] If Morse's intervention reached Professor Henry while he was yet engaged in drafting his opinion on Colt's Submarine Battery, it failed to deter him from rendering judgment, which, taken in conjunction with other professional opinions, proved devastating to that inventor's prospects. In response to Secretary Wilkins' inquiry regarding the originality of Colt's supposed method of submarine demolition, Henry confirmed the opinion of his Philadelphia colleague succinctly:

The explosion of gunpowder at a distance, by means of galvanism, has been familiar to men of science and practical engineers for several years. The method now generally used was made public in 1832, and is the invention of Dr. Hare, of Philadelphia. It consists, essentially, in extending between the reservoir of powder and the operator two long thick wires of copper, the further ends of which, terminating in the powder, are united by a short wire of platinum of small diameter. The other ends of the copper wires, in the hands of the operator, at the desired moment of explosion being suddenly brought in contact with the two poles of a galvanic battery, a current of galvanism is transmitted through the circuit of wires, which, heating to redness the piece of platinum in the midst of the powder, produces the explosion. [180]

The practicability of exploding gunpowder at a distance, in this way, was established by the experiments of Dr. Hare;

Figure 39.—JOSEPH HENRY, 1797–1878. Born at Albany, New York, this eminent early American scientist studied at Albany Academy and in 1826, after briefly considering careers in medicine and the theatre, assumed the Professorship of Mathematics and Natural Philosophy at that institution. Henry proved a stimulating teacher, enlivening his classes with frequent demonstrations of electrical phenomena and in 1827 presenting a paper on "Some Modifications of the Electro-Magnetic Apparatus" that clearly marked him as an emerging scientist. His successful efforts to improve William Sturgeon's electromagnet led him to the discovery of the quantity and intensity magnets, which he reported in Benjamin Silliman's *American Journal of Science* in 1831. Henry accepted the chair of Natural Philosophy at Princeton in 1832, shortly after the belated publication of his pivotal paper "On the Production of Currents and Sparks of Electricity," wherein he described his discovery of the phenomenon of electromagnetic induction, on which Michael Faraday had but recently published.

During a visit to Europe in 1837, Professor Henry discussed his continuing investigation of electromagnetic self-induction with Faraday, Wheatstone, and Daniell. His growing international reputation made his counsel particularly valued in the American Philosophical Society and the Franklin Institute of Philadelphia, the latter on 1 April 1844 appointing him chairman of a scientific investigation of the *Princeton* disaster. Late that month, while Henry was yet engaged in this undertaking, the War Department also requested his opinion on the mysterious Submarine Battery of Samuel Colt, regarding whose tests with insulated cable he had been informed by Samuel F. B. Morse some two years earlier. (*Courtesy of Chicago Historical Society.*)

and his results were verified and applied in actual practice by several persons, before the time of the exhibitions of Mr. Colt. In 1839, a series of experiments by Colonel Pasley, of the royal engineers, was published in England, relative to the explosion of a large quantity of powder by the galvanic process, at the bottom of the river Medway; and, as an evidence of the wide diffusion of the knowledge of this process, I may mention, that I have now before me a book published in Calcutta, in 1841, in which is given a minute account of the experiments of Dr. O'Shaughnessy, of the Bengal army, in destroying a wreck sunk in Hoogly river, by a method which the author himself calls the process of Dr. Hare.

The experiments made on the Hoogly, as well as those on the Medway, were made in 1839; and since that time, as it would appear by the various publications on the subject in the different English scientific journals, the application of the galvanic process of exploding gunpowder has become an established part of the business of the English engineer. In short, I consider the laws of the transmission of electricity through long wires as fully developed by the researches of Ohm, Wheatstone, Daniell, and others,—at least as far as they are applicable to the process in question; that I do not think it in the least degree probable that Mr. Colt has added a single essential fact to the previously existing stock of knowledge on this subject.[181]

Personally conscious, through bitter experience, of the importance of early publication of scientific discoveries, Henry may well have been disturbed by Colt's determined secrecy. The Princeton scientist's statement, as indeed that of Robert Hare, revealed no awareness of Colt's own succinct account of the early history of galvanic rock blasting, published in May 1843 in the *Army and Navy Chronicle and Scientific Repository*. Professor Henry was loath, however, to conclude his professional opinion without a strong cautionary note regarding the Submarine Battery, whose technical details, as pointed out to him in Morse's letter of 30 April in Colt's behalf, were totally unknown to him.[182]

In conclusion, I wish it to be distinctly understood that the foregoing remarks are all made in reference to the method of exploding gunpowder at a distance by means of galvanism, and are intended as a specific answer to the question proposed to me in your letter. Mr. Colt may, perhaps, not attempt to found his claims to originality on the invention of the galvanic process, to which he can have no title, but on a new application of this process to a method of harbor defense; and also on a new arrangement of subaqueous magazines for the same purpose. Of the validity of claims thus founded, I am not called on to give my opinion; but, in justice to Mr. Colt, I ought to say, that whatever may be the result of the investigations relative to originality of his plans, I think he deserves credit for the industry and practical skill with which he has brought them before the public.[183]

These judgments by two distinguished members of the American Philosophical Society represented the closest approximation in mid-nineteenth century America to the opinion of a national academy of sciences. Offered by experienced scientists who had played significant roles in the discovery of electrical phenomena, the opinions of Robert Hare and Joseph Henry reflected their distinct sense of unease in being expected to render judgment on an evident application of science whose parameters remained obscure. Even with Colt's impending patent papers in hand, these eminent referees would have had no solid basis for certifying that his system had been demonstrated at Washington, even in rudimentary form.

No such disquiet pervaded the lengthy report (Appendix 7) submitted to Secretary Wilkins on 1 May by Colonel Joseph G. Totten (Figure 40), Chief of the Corps of Engineers and pre-eminent military engineer in the United States.[184] As conversant with numerous other military inventions offered to the War Department as he was with European systems of fortification and demolition, Totten exuded a military professional's contempt for the secrecy that had surrounded Colt's actual firing arrangements: "I should consider myself as risking nothing were I to engage to have these results repeated, without the least reference to Mr. Colt's—using only processes that are now the property of the scientific world—with modifications probably, but with such only as ingenuity, by no means rare, could supply." [185] Correctly surmising with both Hare and Henry that voltaic electricity was the "combustible agent" employed in the Submarine Battery, Totten advised Wilkins:

The details of Mr. Colt's mode of conveying the power of the galvanic battery to distant charges of gunpowder have not been communicated; he has stated to me, in conversation, that this is a secret between himself and the Navy Department.[186]

While personally unaware of any proposals prior to Colt to employ galvanism in firing harbor defense mines, the Chief Engineer professed greater confidence in the system of contact torpedoes proposed four decades earlier by Robert Fulton, owing to that system's constant relative effectiveness regardless of prevailing visibility conditions. The absence of officially supervised tests for the Submarine Battery proved particularly unacceptable to Totten: "Military experience has enacted, as an inflexible law, that no device, however plausible, shall be admitted to confidence as a military resource, except as it shall make

Figure 40.—Joseph Gilbert Totten, 1788–1864. A native of New Haven, this pioneer of United States military engineering graduated from West Point in 1805 and, upon entering the Corps of Engineers three years later, took part in the construction of Fort Clinton at Castle Garden on Manhattan Island. During the War of 1812, Totten was twice brevetted for gallantry while serving as Chief Engineer on the Niagara frontier and in the defense of Plattsburgh, concluding that conflict with the mining and demolition of Fort Erie. In 1816, Brevet Lieutenant Colonel Totten was posted to the new board of engineers, headed by General Simon Bernard, subsequently making a major contribution to that board's series of landmark reports, which not only inaugurated the nation's Third System of coastal fortifications but actually established the first comprehensive United States defense policy. The designer and constructor of Fort Adams at Newport, Rhode Island, which was regarded as the most advanced masonry works of that era, Colonel Totten was appointed Chief Engineer of the United States Army in 1838 and, distinguishing himself yet again at the siege of Vera Cruz in 1847, continued to serve as head of the Engineer Bureau until 1864.

Brevetted as Brigadier General in 1847, Totten was regarded as a model of professional competence, energy, and incorruptibility. "Conservative in all his views," as described by one observer, "he was slow to adopt innovations, yet he was ever foremost to embrace all great professional improvements. . . . His judgment was as sound as his reason, and his almost Draconian sense of justice required of others the measure of right practiced by himself." A connoisseur of scientific, professional, and literary works, Totten published a notable report on national defense in 1851 and was destined to play an important role in planning the defenses of Washington during the Civil War. He was additionally a leading figure in the emphemeral National Institute, was appointed in 1846 to the first Board of Regents of the Smithsonian Institution, and served with Joseph Henry on the Light House Board.

its way by success in actual war, or in a long and severe course of experience analogous thereto." [187] Although uninformed as to the complexity or indeed the existence of Colt's "torpedo tower," Colonel Totten identified the observation post inherent in such a galvanic system as a link vulnerable to attack by hostile landing parties, in the absence of fortifications or large defending forces:

The defence rests, then, either upon the fort or upon the army, and not upon the deposites of powder; for, if this protecting force be overcome, there will then remain nothing to prevent the breaking up and destruction of the galvanic arrangements. Or the enemy may prefer to destroy the system of conducting wires as they lie upon the bottom. For this purpose, he may send at night his heavy boats—aided, perhaps, by one or two small steamboats, each provided with the means of dragging the bottom, so as to break the wires, and tear away the powder cases. Traversing the channel in all directions within the scope of the deposites, a single night would suffice to clear away from the portion of the channel designed to be followed, every trace of submarine communication.[188]

Aware of Colt's repeated if impolitic assertions that the Submarine Battery represented an economical substitute, rather than an auxiliary element, for the Engineer Corps' extensive system of coastal fortifications, Colonel Totten thus concluded in advising the Secretary of War:

That the project of Mr. Colt, as a sole means of defence, is wholly undeserving of consideration; as an auxiliary, although it might in some situations be resorted to, it should in all, or nearly all such cases, be regarded as inferior to means that have long been known; and, even when resorted to, that it may be applied without any indebtedness to Mr. Colt, either as an inventor, an improver, or an applier of the process.[189]

Reviewed and approved by scientists and ordnance specialists of the Army's Topographical and Ordnance bureaus, the Totten critique powerfully complemented the opinions of Hare and Henry, adding persuasive military objections to the Submarine Battery proposal. These eminent professional objections, countered by no substantive detail from Colt regarding the theory or actual demonstration of his system, bulked understandably large in Secretary Wilkins' report of 8 May 1844 (Appendix 11) to the House of Representatives. Yet at no point in its evaluation of Colt's supposed system did the War Department reveal itself cognizant of mine warfare development in Russia during the preceeding half decade, a development— alluded to by the *Army and Navy Chronicle and*

Scientific Repository on 13 June 1844—currently being carried forward as an adjunct to the tsarist coastal fortification system. Thus, based upon well-established information on galvanic applications to underwater demolitions in England, India, and the United States, as well as on forceful objections from the Corps of Engineers, the Secretary concluded:

If the means assumed to be those employed by Mr. Colt (and if we are in error, he has his own caution alone to blame) are actually not those which he uses, then I affirm that any intelligent, scientific person, aided and encouraged by equal munificence and appropriations, could, without invading any patent or exclusive right of others, and by merely applying means which have been gratuitously contributed to science by distinguished men of our country, accomplish all that Mr. Colt has achieved under the bounty and generous encouragement of his government, in his peaceful experiments against a defenseless and untenanted ship.[190]

In rejecting Samuel Colt's proposal that the United States acquire the secret of his Submarine Battery on the basis of a negotiated settlement, Secretary Wilkins played a major role, together with the inventor himself, in postponing submarine mine development in the United States for nearly a generation. The Wilkins report, a 17-page document freighted with the aforementioned advisory opinions, was received by the House on 15 May and promptly referred to its Committee on Naval Affairs, where it remained in limbo until early in 1845.[191] Meanwhile, in an effort to revive his dwindling prospects, Colt had written to Representative Henry C. Murphy of that Committee on 3 June, setting forth in considerable detail the 15-year history of his submarine experiments (Appendix 12), making full acknowledgment of Robert Hare's pioneer contributions to galvanic demolitions and yet concluding with characteristic grammatical flourish (once again without disclosing the unique element of his system),

I claim to be the originator of a submarine battery with peculiarities which has enabled me to perform what has never before been accomplished and on a full explanation of my plans and secrets to my Government[,] *originality* of plans was not only admitted but I were encouraged to prove in practice what seemed plausible in my theory, and I were to have if successful a reward adequate to the advantage to be derived therefrom [.] *I have proven every thing contemplated or regarding which a doubt was entertained,* and now I desire the further action of Government on my claims to their promise "quid propo" [*quid pro quo*].[192]

Evidently drafted in deep resentment, Colt's challenge revealed a broad gulf of misunderstanding. In an effort to resolve the matter, Representative Murphy called upon Colt to reveal the details of his Submarine Battery to Henry L. Ellsworth, the U.S. Commissioner of Patents, "in order to ascertain whether it possessed novelty sufficient to sustain a patent, as in that case alone would it justify the further consideration of the government." [193] Thus, on 8 June 1844, the inventor submitted a formal patent application, enclosing a detailed description of the Submarine Battery that included plans indicating its principal components. After describing his metallic "torpedoes" and their platinum filament firing arrangements (Appendix 13), Colt explained the operation of his "torpedo tower":

A main point in the producing of submarine explosions, so as to destroy a vessel under sail is to ascertain the instant when such vessel is directly over one of the torpedoes, and this I effect in two ways, in one of which it is ascertained by reflection, by means of mirrors, which can be managed by one observer....

In drawing No. 3 [Figure 41], I have given a sketch of the manner in which the place of a vessel is ascertained by reflection. C, is a convex mirror so situated as to take in the whole field of view of the channel, or harbour where the torpedoes are anchored; from this mirror the vessel which may come within the field of view will be reflected, at an angle due to its situation, onto a metallic, or other, mirror, situated at D. This second mirror is surrounded by a number

of pieces of metal a,a,a, which constitute the terminations of as many connecting wires as there are torpedoes anchored, and the mirror is so arranged as to exhibit distinctly the place of the reflected image of the vessel, and the connecting wire corresponding with this situation. E, is the Battery, and F,F, the connecting wires leading to and from the respective torpedoes. The operator is consequently enabled to complete the circuit at the moment when the vessel is over the torpedo indicated by the reflection.[194]

Although Colt's patent application also described his two-observer system, it was his novel "torpedo tower" that aroused keenest interest (Figure 42). Having examined the application, Commissioner Ellsworth concluded that the Submarine Battery pos-

Figure 41.—INTERIOR ARRANGEMENT FOR COLT'S "REFLECTED SUBMARINE BATTERY." The single-cell battery indicated in this drawing is not clearly identified in Colt's papers but appears to have been an early version of J. Frederic Daniell's "constant battery" (1836), which possessed the advantage of providing an undiminished supply of voltage for a succession of mine detonations. Colt may have employed the more powerful Grove battery for his final demonstration at Washington in 1844. There is no clear evidence that he employed a fixed control grid on that or previous occasions, a fact that would have baffled his official reviewers even had they been granted access to his patent draughts.

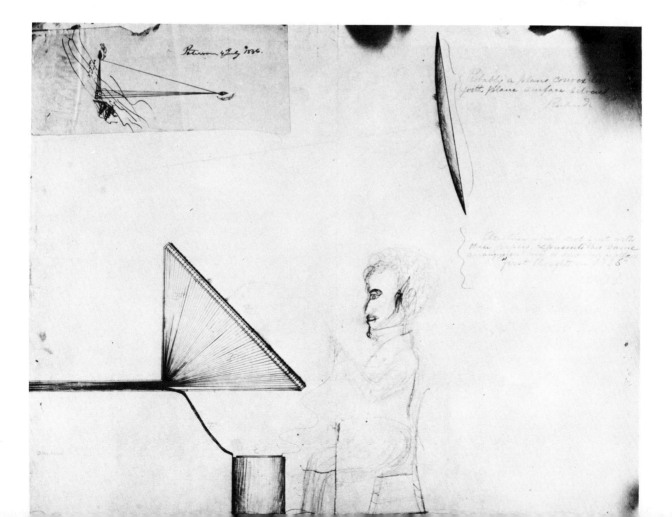

Figure 42.—SAMUEL COLT'S "TORPEDO TOWER." This watercolor illustration, part of a 13-foot drawing ("A") that may have accompanied Colt's patent application in 1844, reveals clearly the unique core of his Submarine Bat-tery conception, a galvanic observation post. One undated note in his papers indicates that he envisaged a tower no less than 100 feet in height, altogether a most tempting target for his critics had they ever learned of his conception.

sessed "novelty sufficient to sustain a patent." [195] This opinion was sustained by Dr. Thomas P. Jones, former Superintendent of the Patent Office and long-time editor of the *Journal of the Franklin Institute*, who had at Secretary Wilkins' request closely examined the Submarine Battery patent, finding it "not only novel, but . . . also calculated to effect the purpose with a certainty nearly unerring." [196] On the basis of the Patent Office finding, the House Committee on Naval Affairs thus concluded that Samuel Colt's Submarine Battery indeed possessed the merit of originality.[197]

Unhappily for Colt, however, the committee did not limit its requirement to the criteria of originality, turning thereupon to the question of utility. In review-ing the War Department's objections, the committee found itself severely embarrassed by lack of tangible information. Particularly open to challenge, in view of the character of the "torpedo tower," was the Department's admitted supposition that "it is impos-sible for the operator to ascertain the precise position of the vessel so as to effect the explosion at the right time." [198] While there is no evidence that Colt had actually employed a fully equipped observation post, replete with convex mirror and grided firing panel, during the Washington demonstration in 1844, he had demonstrably succeeded in firing a torpedo beneath a moving target with substantial accuracy. Under the circumstances, including the persuasive

Totten strictures regarding the vulnerability of Colt's observation post to landing parties, the committee proceeded to a remarkably ambivalent conclusion:

From all, therefore, that appears in the reports of the Secretaries, there is nothing to induce the committee to believe that there is no utility in the invention of Mr. Colt. The Committee, on the contrary, from the affirmative testimony which had been submitted to them, and to which they have referred, and from the experiments witnessed by themselves, are of opinion that the invention is entitled to the favorable consideration of government. There is not sufficient evidence, however, before the committee, to enable them to judge of the propriety of adopting it as a means of fortification; and they are therefore not prepared to recommend it for that purpose.[199]

Confronted by the mounting disinterest of the War and Navy Departments, the committee was seriously embarrassed in its efforts to resolve the Submarine Battery issue. Although prepared to recommend compensation to Colt for personal expenses incurred during his experiments, the committee was disinclined to advocate payment of a premium to the inventor for the secret of his Submarine Battery. And a secret it was to remain. Having withdrawn his patent on the very day after its nominal filing, Colt carried the details of this unique mine warfare system to his grave.[200] The House Committee report, drafted on the eve of the election of 1844, remained in limbo throughout that year, while Colt sought unsuccessfully to induce both War and Navy Departments to carry out a survey of harbors and rivers in which the Submarine Battery might be employed. On 11 January 1845, Representative Murphy introduced legislation for formal acquisition of the Submarine Battery system and a settlement of Colt's claims for an "adequate reward," subsequently set at $10,000.[201]

In reality, however, the Tyler administration had at no stage formally committed itself to payment of a premium to Colt should the Submarine Battery experiments prove successful. Thus, in response to an inquiry from the House Committee on Naval Affairs, Secretary of the Navy John Y. Mason effectively terminated further consideration of Colt's claims for reward on 13 February, stating: "Believing that any projector of a great national improvement is amply compensated for his personal troubles in the advantage to be derived from the Govt with its means testing his invention, I could not recommend the clause giving a salary for several years past to Mr. Colt." [202] Having invested more than three years in the development of the Submarine Battery, its inven-

tor was actually to derive nothing of profit from his government-sponsored experiments, either in the form of United States contracts for his system or subsequent offers from foreign governments, which he made no effort to solicit. For the disenchanted Colt there would have been little additional solace in Secretary Mason's concluding judgment that

the government ought not to authorize expenditures of money in testing inventions unless it was first ascertained satisfactorily by the examination of competent officers or others that the *probable* results would be advantageous.[203]

Such indeed was the costly administrative lesson that emerged from the Submarine Battery fiasco, a lesson whose principal victim proved to be a young and virtually bankrupt inventor. Samuel Colt's tortuous approach to Congress on behalf of his novel mine warfare conception, calculated on the basis of his previous frustrations with the Army Ordnance Office, had postponed his reckoning with the military professionals; yet in the final event it proved singularly ill-advised. To Colt's misfortune, no national scientific institution then existed in the United States within which the Submarine Battery might have enjoyed a deliberate, officially sponsored development. Dedicated entrepreneur and lobbyist that he remained, Colt had demonstrated from his youth a strong attachment to scientific inquiry, and his association with Draper and Morse at the University of the City of New York suggests that under more favorable circumstances he would have collaborated with a major scientific institution in perfecting his unique mine warfare system.

Fundamental to Samuel Colt's extended commitment to the Submarine Battery's development was the clear realization that he would be heavily reliant on financial support from the government. Frustrating as had been his experience in attempting to have his tinfoil cartridges manufactured at the Washington Arsenal under the aegis of the Ordnance Office, the question may reasonably be raised whether the inventor might not have fared better with his Submarine Battery had he sought the collaboration of the Engineer Corps in its development. The leaders of that elite corps were by no means hostile to peacetime development of a mine warfare capability within the service. Doubtless impressed by the evident success of Colonel Pasley's training program at Chatham, Colonel Totten had advocated establishment of a Company of Sappers, Miners and Pontoniers as early as 1841. Late in 1844, with memory of the Colt imbroglio still fresh, the Chief Engineer returned to that proposal, providing Senator Thomas Hart Benton with the draft of a bill establishing such a specialized contingent. Totten appears to have envisaged more than a simple training mission for such a Company. That he may have aspired to creating a modest counterpart of the progressive Chatham establishment is suggested in the conclusion of a substantial report to Secretary of War Wilkins on 4 February 1845 by a special board consisting of Totten (Corps of Engineers), Lt. Col. George Talcott (Ordnance Office) and Colonel John J. Abert (Topographical Engineers) regarding the submarine rocket proposals of George William Taylor of Boston. That indefatigable inventor, whose total underwater schema included a diving bell, armored diving suit, collapsible lifeboat, hand-propelled submersible, and limpet type "rockets," had been conducting underwater demonstrations as early as 1839 from Charleston to Boston. Profiting from the tactical lessons of Colt's misadventure, Taylor finally submitted his underwater system, which envisaged galvanic or percussion detonation of his submarine rockets, to the aforementioned military board early in 1845. Though highly impressed by that inventor's candor and ingenuity, Totten and his colleagues rendered an adverse verdict, partly on the basis of the imperfect state of his system's development. The idea of taking over the development of Taylor's rocket was not broached. The kernel of a policy indeed emerged, however, perhaps through consecutive impact of the Colt and Taylor proposals:

> The device of Fulton—we mean the anchored Torpedo—though needing modification—is in our opinion far superior to any of its successors—the present one included. Being of that opinion, we advise if the government is desirous of having ideas of this nature matured, that its attention be turned in that direction, through its own officers, who undoubtedly are competent to apply all requisite improvements. We think the subject should be taken up by the Government, made its own: & all its secrets if there are to be any, confined within responsible limits. If the subject be really of great importance to the nation, it is worthy of this attention; and, in the meantime, the inventions of individuals, in the same field should be discouraged; & not assisted, to be, in the end, perhaps, turned against ourselves.[204]

Even considering Colt's undisguised threat to emigrate to Russia in 1841, the board's proprietary view on mine-warfare development could be seriously faulted from the security aspect, as the wholesale defection of military and naval officers to the Confeder-

acy demonstrated two decades later. As a matter of record, neither the Colt nor Taylor proposals were to assist the U.S. Army in rationalizing the establishment of a cadre of sappers and miners capable of carrying forward significant peacetime development programs comparable to those already afoot in Europe.

Colt's inability to provide detailed voucher substantiation of his expenditures for development of the Submarine Battery during 1841–44 was to embroil him in prolonged correspondence with auditors of the Treasury Department that was not concluded until 1854.[205] During the intervening years, he survived an almost equally disastrous plunge into the early telegraphic communications industry and succeeded—largely on the basis of substantial War Department orders for his repeating arms during the Mexican War—in establishing a private arsenal at Hartford that embodied some of the most advanced techniques in machine tool employment and enlightened labor management practices in the mid-nineteenth century.[206] Colt's eventual success in securing major government arms contracts was derived from emergency war-time requirements rather than the recommendations of an officially constituted ordnance inspection board, a circumstance that doubtless assuaged the frustration of his coastal defense proposals.

Viewed in longer perspective, the technological nonfruition of Samuel Colt's mine warfare system proved remarkably fortuitous for the United States. It seems apparent that had Great Britain intervened in the course of the Mexican War, his Submarine Battery might well have received renewed consideration in Washington, notwithstanding a remarkably inflexible schedule of prices that survives in the Colt Papers for the manufacture of varying numbers of mines.[207] As events transpired, however, the Royal Navy encountered its first major mine threat off Kronstadt during the Crimean War, a long obscured episode in the evolution of modern naval technology that failed to stimulate serious experimentation with systems of submarine mining in either the United States or Great Britain.[208] The continued disinterest of American military engineers and ordnance specialists—professionals shortly to be pitted against one another in four years of desperate coastal and riverine warfare—in establishing a peacetime developmental base in sea mine technology was, ironically, to prove of profound importance to the ultimate preservation of the Union.

Viewed in the perspective of the approaching Civil

Figure 43.—Split-control reflected Submarine Battery system. The ultimate concept of Samuel Colt's harbor defense system, this section of his 13-foot drawing ("A") of the Submarine Battery reveals a channel or harbor sown with no fewer than 2500 mines, controlled in clusters of five cases. Observational command of the mined area appears divided between two "torpedo towers" of different height, as seen in the lower or transverse plan.

War, during which extensive Confederate innovation in the art of undersea warfare was launched from an essentially theoretical base by Matthew Fontaine Maury,[209] the adamant refusal of Samuel Colt in 1844 to vouchsafe the secret of his Submarine Battery to unsympathetic military professionals appears to have contributed substantially to that narrow margin of inadequacy found in the Confederate coastal defense system two decades later. Paradoxically, however, it was the intricate character of Southern coastal defenses, notably as developed at Charleston, combining combat-proven modifications of vulnerable Third System fortifications with a variety of auxiliary underwater systems—mines, obstructions and semi-submersible torpedo craft—that convinced both European and American military engineers of the absolute necessity of integrating undersea warfare systems in future coastal defense planning.[210] While recognizing an element of overstatement in Samuel Colt's claims for coastal mine warfare in the context of his era, one may scarcely review naval operations during the present century—in the Yellow Sea, the Dardanelles, the Heligoland Bight and Danish Straits, and the coasts of Korea and Indochina—without perceiving the larger prophetic character of his Submarine Battery proposal.

Appendixes 1–14

APPENDIX 1: Unsigned inventory (not Colt's) of the Samuel Colt Collection, Connecticut State Library Museum, Hartford.

S. Colt's Submarine Battery
Conceived 1836.

List of drawings and sketches.

Note: To this belongs an exhibit consisting of an electric cable insulated by being covered by a lead pipe.

Mark on
Sheet:

A. A drawing in water colors 13 feet long by 2 feet 1″ wide, showing a sectional view of torpedoes in position and submarine and subterranean electric connection with observatory and battery; also a smaller scale section with two stations on opposite shores, and a larger scale plan view.

B. A pencil sketch representing the blowing up of a vessel by Col. S. Colt in the Potomac near Washington Navy Yard, about 1843, endorsed on face by the word "correct."

C. Plan showing location of torpedoes, connections, and location of two observatories.

D. Sketch of an operator making connection or closing the circuit at that point of the switchboard which is indicated to him by the appearance on the inclined surface of the switchboard of the image of the object; this image being reflected upon the switchboard by a planoconvex reflector above and in rear of the operator, and indicating the presence of the passing object (ship, et.c.) over that torpedo, of which the connecting electric wire ends at the point of the switchboard where the image appears. A small sketch fastened to this sheet shows the exact location of a passing object by observation from two stations, this sketch is endorsed in writing "Patterson, July 4th, 1836." Sheet D bears some explanatory notes by Chs. B. Richards.

E. Pencil sketch of submerged electric torpedoes and indication of the passage of an object by its reflection. Endorsed "Submarine Battery first thoughts in 1836."

F. Plan of one station connecting with parallel rows of torpedoes.

G. Detailed view of submerged anchored torpedoes electrically connected to a cable.

H. Shows (on the back of an old memorandum of an address) an electric fuse, in which a cap is to be struck when a hammer is liberated; the hammer detent is shown as if to be liberated by the closing of the circuit at the station.?

I. Detail view of torpedo marked in pencil "Submarine torpedo fired by electricity or Galvanic Battery."

J. & K. Two sheets, plans for location of torpedoes; on back of K endorsed: "Submarine Battery
S. Colt."

L. Small sheet showing an instrument, endorsed "Metallic Thermometer for ~~testing &~~ showing ~~the~~ quantity of galvanic fluid. New York University.
S. Colt, June 5th, 1842"

M, N, O, Six sheets showing details of a galvanic battery.
P, Q, R. Endorsed: "Siphon Battery, University N.Y. May 1842."

S & T. 2 sheets, showing soundings of entrance to the New York Harbor.

U. Copy of a part of coast survey.

APPENDIX 2: Letter of Samuel Colt to President John Tyler, 19 June 1841, retained copy, Samuel Colt Papers, box 5, Connecticut Historical Society, Hartford. [The original of this letter has not been found in the John Tyler Papers in the Manuscripts Division of the Library of Congress.]

Washington, June 19, 1841.

Sir:

It is with no little diffidence that I venture to submit the following for your consideration; feeling as I do, that its apparent extravagance may prevent you from paying it that attention which it merits. & but for the duty I owe my country in these threatning times, I should still longer delay making this communication.

There seems to prevail at this time with all parties a sense of the importance of effectually protecting our Sea Coast; & as economy is a primary consideration, in the present exhausted state of our treasury, I think I have a right to expect a favourable consideration of the propositions which I have determined to make.

For more than five years past I have employed my leisure, in study & experiment, to perfect the invention of which I now consider myself master; & which if adopted for the service of our Government, will not only save them millions outlay for the construction of means of defence, but in the event of foreign war, it will prove a perfect safeguard against all the combined fleets of Europe, without exposing the life of our citizens.

By referring to the Navy State Papers, page 211, you will discover that *Robert Fulton* made experiments which proved that a certain quantity of Gunpowder discharged under the bottom of a ship would produce her instant destruction. That discovery laid the foundation for my present plan of harbour defence. & notwithstanding the failure of Fulton to use his invention to much advantage in its imperfect condition during the last war, one glance at what he did perform, is sufficient to convince the most incredulous that if his engine could be brought within easy & safe control, it must prove an irresistible barrier against foreign invasion.

Discoveries since Fulton's time combined with an invention original with myself, enable me to effect the instant destruction of either Ships, or Steamers, at my pleasure on their entering a harbour, whether singly, or in whole fleets; while those vessels to which I am disposed to allow a passage, are secure from a possibility of being injured. All this I can do in perfect security, & without giving an invading enemy the slightest sign of his danger.

The whole expense of protecting a Harbour like that of New York, would be less then [than] the cost of a single steam ship; & when once prepared, one single man is sufficient to manage the destroying agent against any fleet that Europe can send.

With the above statements as an intimation of what can be done, I will mention in as brief a manner as possible, the terms on which I will make an exhibition to prove to yourself, & your Cabinet, that a Sailing vessel, or Steamboat, cannot pass (without permission) either in or out of a harbour where my engines of destruction are employed.

To make the exhibition (which I contemplate should I meet with sufficient encouragement) will require an expenditure of $20,000. which sum I will employ for that purpose from my own means; on condition that the Government will lend me such aid as I shall require (which can be supplied without incurring new expenses) & that when I get through my exhibition, the Government shall refund to me the amount of money which I shall have expended; & pay me an annual some [sum] of $_____ as a premium for my secret.

In hope I may be excused for mentioning that as any hint of my plans at this time must prove prejuditial, it is my wish that the present communication may be kept from the view of all persons excepting the members of your Cabinet.

I have the honor to be

Sir.
            Most Respectfully
        Your Excellency's Devoted
            & Obedient Servant
                Samuel Colt
                Fullers Hotel

To his Excellency
    John Tyler
        President of the United States

APPENDIX 3: Description of firing arrangement in Colt's Submarine Battery, published in the *Alexandria Gazette and Virginia Advertiser*, 5 October 1842.

LETTER FROM WASHINGTON.

COLT'S SUBMARINE BATTERY, &c. &c.

I do not know whether you have seen or published an account of Colt's Steam [Submarine] Battery, and as its description is simple and yet interesting, I have transcribed the following from a Northern paper, viz:—the Battery consists of a light sheet iron box filled with gunpowder, and having two copper wires wound around with cotton, then varnished with a mixture of gum shellack, alcohol, and Venice Turpentine, and extending through tight corks in one side of the box, having a piece of platina wire extending between them in the box amongst the gunpowder, and the two copper wires extending off from this box, (which may be anchored in the channel of a river) to a large one of Grant's Electricity collecting [connecting] machines, electrified by a large Galvanic Battery, which may be seven or eight miles distant from the box, and where the operation [operator] is, having one of the wires in his hand ready to attach them to the *collectors* [connectors] the instant the signal is given to explode the box.

Now, when an enemy is over the box, and the wires are that instant attached, positive electricity immediately passes along one wire, and negative electricity immediately passes along the other wire, these two kinds of electricity concentrate on the platina wire, instantly heat it red hot, and it fires the gunpowder, and blows the vessel to fragments.

Having seen the effects of this wonderful contrivance in the explosion of a stout schooner near Greenleaf's Point, I am as well convinced of its utility for the protection of harbors, and indeed of bays and rivers from the invasion of hostile fleets, as of any other invention which of late has so astonished the world. It has been said that the wires could be raked up by sending boats ahead with rakes and oyster-tongs. I think it would be rather a hazardous business, if not utterly impracticable for the want of a knowledge of the locality of the boxes (for I presume any number of boxes may be sunk in the channel) and with wires; besides the operator or superintendent in one night could sink boxes in the channel in [the] rear of the enemy's ships, which would ensure their destruction, and instead of raking for the wires, you would find the crews taking to their boats and jumping overboard. I trust we may hereafter dispense with our expensive and useless forts on the sea-board. I say *useless,* because they are of no earthly use but to protect the soldiers from the enemy, who can land their men out of gunshot of the fort, and ravage the country, opposed by none but militia. We experienced this last war, in the instance of Forts Detroit, Niagara, Oswego, Castine and Fort Bowyer. I ask what advantage Fortress Monroe could afford in time of war, as a defence or obstruction? It is true vessels might take shelter under its guns, but vessels have cut out harbors fortified more skilfully and more difficult of access than Fort Monroe. Then again, suppose this fort should be taken by the enemy, (a matter not in the least, problematical) would it not afford the invaders a rendezvous for their fleet, and enable them to annoy the whole country. Many persons think Forts Monroe and Calhoun protect the mouths of Chesapeake and James River, a fact entirely erroneous. A ship bound up the bay need not approach the Fort nearer than six miles, and perhaps as much as ten. My opinion has ever been that Forts should be built on the confines of a town or city, and located in a position where the approach of an enemy might be more easily repelled. Forts built 5, 10, 15, 20, and 100 miles off, from a city, it is intended, to protect, is of a piece with the system of opposing Indians with Infantry, many of whom never rode a horse in their lives and are only fit for building Barracks and cultivating the lands for their own support and convenience. Yet such were the soldiers to oppose the Indians in Florida, some of them enlisted not three days in the country, and who had never rode a horse or fired a musket in the country they emigrated from. The light Artillery is the best force to subdue Indians flanked by mounted gun men.

I have been thinking it strange that such a fuss should be made in N. York about the *fist fight* of Lilly and McKoy, and that the press should ring with its enormity far and near; whilst at the same time duelling, with deadly weapons, is tolerated. Nature gave to all animals as well as man, the means of offence and defence, and the use of those powers are not cognizable as felonies. But when we see gentlemen go to the fields and kill each other, instead of rendering them odious to the community, and objects liable to the penalties of the law—their society is courted and they become bold and insulting in their intercourse whether in the forum or in private circles. On the other hand the lower classes who fight with their fists are hooted [hunted?] down, and a hue and cry raised all over the Union after them for punishment.

C.

Washington, Oct. 1, 1842.

APPENDIX 4: Letter of Secretary of War William Wilkins to Joseph Henry, 29 April 1844, in *Letter from the Secretary of War Relative to the Secret of Colt's Submarine Battery, May 15, 1844,* House Document No. 127, 28th Congress, 2nd Session, page 11.

War Department, April 29, 1844.

Sir: I have the honor to enclose you a copy of a resolution adopted by the House of Representatives, in relation to "the combustible agent used by Mr. Colt;" and beg you will pardon me for asking your attention to the first branch of the resolution.

It is understood that the explosive agent used by Mr. Colt is gunpowder; and that this is fired by means of galvanism, or other similar agency.

Your pursuits having led you, doubtless, to an acquaintance with what has been heretofore done in this branch of practical science, the War Department would be much obliged by the communication of your views in reference to the claims which Mr. Colt's methods may have to originality.

My object is not to impose labor or detail upon you. Your opinion, transmitted to me with as much brevity as you may think proper to use, and with as little delay as may suit your convenience, will be thankfully received as a contribution in the advancement of a public inquiry.

Very respectfully, &c.,

WILLIAM WILKINS

Professor JOSEPH HENRY,
Princeton, New Jersey

APPENDIX 5: Letter of Samuel F. B. Morse to Joseph Henry, 30 April 1844 in Joseph Henry Papers, Smithsonian Institution Archives, Washington, D.C.

Washington April 30, 1844

My dear Sir,

Mr. Colt has just called on me and informs me that you have been written to by the Secy. of War for an opinion respecting his submarine battery. He feels very anxious on the subject, as he conceives that there is a natural prejudice in the war department against any innovation upon the old established plans of fortification, and harbor defence. He thinks your letter will influence the decision in Congress, as it will be submitted to them and be published, and he wished me to write you for him. I told him I would do so, and in fulfilment of my promise I write this. I informed him that you would speak your mind prudently and without fear or favor [and] that he need not apprehend anything adverse from you, as I presumed [that] all you would testify in regard to the mode he adopted would be that he had not imparted any knowledge of it to you, and therefore nothing could be said respecting it, but that a method could be devised for accomplishing what he accomplishes on known scientific principles.

I take this hurried opportunity just to say that my telegraph is in successful operation for 22 miles, and I am in constant correspondence from that distance, from the Junction of the Annapolis rail road with the Baltimore & Wash^n. rail road, to the Capitol. I wish I had time to write you more on the subject, and especially do I wish that you could be here just now to suggest and make any experiments which may further your valuable researches.

In great haste but with real respect & esteem
Y. Mo. Ob. Servt.
Sam. F.B. Morse.

Prof. Joseph Henry
Princeton.

APPENDIX 6: Letter of Professor Robert Hare to Secretary of War William Wilkins, 1 May 1844, in *Colt's Submarine Battery*, House Document No. 127, 28th Congress, 2nd Session, pages 12–14.

Philadelphia, May 1, 1844.

Sir: 1. In reply to your letter of yesterday, and to the requisition made by the House of Representatives of the United States, I hasten to say, that, as respects the employment of a galvanic current to ignite a wire, and by means thereof to explode gunpowder, whether for the purpose of rock-blasting, or for warlike defence or annoyance, the galvanic process employed by Mr. Colt has not the slightest claims to originality. This will be made evident by an inspection of the 12th volume, page 221, of the Journal of the Franklin Institute, of which there is no doubt a copy in the national library in the Capitol. It will therein appear that I published an account of the *simultaneous* explosion of twelve charges of gunpowder, at the distance of one hundred and fifty feet, by one battery. I performed the experiment at that distance, to show that the apparatus might be remote from the cavity in which ignition is to be effected by it; but it was perfectly well known to myself, and all others acquainted with galvanism, that many miles might intervene, the number and size of the galvanic series being proportionally enlarged.

2. The process thus described did not differ from one of which I published an account in volume 2, page 315, Silliman's Journal, in 1820, as the means of igniting gaseous mixtures in my eudiometrical apparatus. The rock blasting was suggested by the application to me for assistance of a projector of the name of Shaw, who had attempted, with little success, to employ electricity produced by friction for that purpose, with occasional and uncertain success, and wished to learn by what means he could avoid the disappointment resulting from the paralyzing influence of moisture.

3. It may be observed that paragraph the 4th, on page 223 of the 12th volume of the Journal of the Franklin Institute, before mentioned, consists of the following words: *"It must be obvious, that in all cases of blasting under water, the plan of a tin tube, and ignition by a galvanic circuit, must be very eligible."* The concluding paragraph of the communication (page 226) is as follows: "It can scarcely be necessary to point out that the method of communicating ignition described here for the purpose of rock-blasting, may be applied as the means of exploding a mine. As, for instance, the mines associated with the fortifications creating near Newport, as a part of the means of annoyance, might have a communication through copper wires, with a galvanic apparatus, in those situations to which the besieged might be expected to retire; putting it thus completely in the power of the commanding officer to select that time for the explosion when its effects would be most servicable."

4. Thus it appears that I had represented my process as peculiarly applicable to blasting under water, and exploding mines as a means of military annoyance. Moreover, it will appear from the Journal of the Franklin Institute, (vol. 1, 3d series, for 1841, page 154,) that the process devised by me was used in 1840 by Alexander Paris, civil engineer,

who mentions the previous employment of it in England for removing the wreck of the Royal George, and in several other successful enterprises.

5. Professor O'Shaughnessy, of Calcutta, informed me, when in this city last spring, that he had (in consequence of reading of my experiments) undertaken with complete success, by a similar process, to remove from the channel of the river Hoogly the hull of a large sunken vessel which interfered with the navigation.

6. Professor Draper, of New York, has informed me that he instructed Mr. Colt as to the process which he uses; it being understood by him at the time that it was one which I had previously employed.

7. I am ready to admit that Mr. Colt must have been judicious and skillful in availing himself of the means which he has owed to the invention of others. As respects the employment of the process as a means of harbor defence, the only objection that occurs to my mind arises from the great difficulty of conceiving how it can be applied so as to avail against movable bodies like ships of war. If Mr. Colt can so employ an exploding apparatus as to defend a harbor, I can see no objection to the project, excepting that it must be very precarious. Any number of casks of gunpowder may be made to float in a channel, and may be exploded by the means which I have devised, at any desirable instant, either successively, or all at once. Where the channel is so narrow that an approaching vessel could not pass without coming very near one or more of them, evidently she might be discomfited. The casks might contain rockets and fire-balls, which might fly to a great distance, and set fire to the sails of shipping. But where there is a squadron of ships, the casks being so exploded as to injure the first, there would be no means of preventing the passage of the remainder.

8. It occurs to me to suggest that a floating battery might be so placed as to have the guns discharged at any moment, in a way to destroy a passing ship.

9. Of the peculiar mode in which Mr. Colt proposes to employ galvanic ignition in harbor defence I have no knowledge; and of course, on that subject, I cannot form any opinion.

10. The fact that my apparatus, in the hands of my ingenious countryman Paris, was found superior for blasting under water to that employed by Colonel Pasley, proves the folly of the reason assigned by him for his not employing it—that it *had not been used under water*. (See Franklin Journal.) But, as the distinguishing feature of my process consists in the use of the galvanic circuit, it makes but little difference whether the one or the other form of the galvanic battery were employed.

11. While the process of blasting galvanism is before Congress, I beg leave to call their attention to the humane object for which it was devised. In England, any effort of this kind is cried up both as an individual and national honor. Look at the instance of Davy's safety-lamp. The neglect of the use of my process for rock-blasting has caused many persons to be killed or crippled. I presume, however, that the resolution of Congress, in consequence of which I am honored by your letter, is not sufficiently broad to make it proper to take into view any other object besides harbor defence.

12. Since the preceding pages were written, I have found in the United Service Journal, published at London, an account of the operations of Col. Pasley in removing the wrecks of several vessels, especially that of the Royal George. It appears that, after bungling for some time with other means of communicating ignition, Colonel Pasley became acquainted with my process for effecting that result, and heretofore resorted to the galvanic circuit for the purpose alluded to. (See vol. 1, 3d series, Franklin Journal, already referred to, page 158.) With true British pride, however, they determined to go through a vast deal of trouble to get up a plan of their own, when the experiments of Paris show that my plan, already perfected, was preferable to that to which they resorted.

I subjoin extracts A and B from the works above mentioned.

I am, sir, your obedient servant,
ROBERT HARE.

WILLIAM WILKINS, esq.

APPENDIX 7: Letter of Colonel Joseph G. Totten to Secretary of War William Wilkins, 1 May 1844, in *Colt's Submarine Battery*, House Document No. 127, 28th Congress, 2nd Session, pages 6–11.

Engineer Department
Washington, May 1, 1844

SIR: The resolution of Congress of the 19th ult., having been referred by you for report to this office, I have the honor to submit thereon the following remarks. The resolution is in the following words:

"*Resolved*, That the Secretaries of War and Navy be requested to communicate to this House the fact, whether the combustible agent used by Mr. Colt was a secret before he made the same known at the seat of government; and whether the mode of its application to harbor defence be new; and if new, what objections there are against its adoption, if objections do exist."

I. *Whether the combustible agent used by Mr. Colt was a secret before he made the same known at the seat of government?*

I understand this inquiry to refer to the *combustible agent,* by which fire is conveyed to deposites of gunpowder, and not to the gunpowder itself, nor to any substance substituted for gunpowder; and this agent I understand to be galvanism, or voltaic electricity. As to the *nature* of this agent, there is, I suppose, no concealment. The details of Mr. Colt's mode of conveying the power of the galvanic battery to distant charges of gunpowder have not been communicated; he has stated to me, in conversation, that this is a secret between himself and the Navy Department.

The process thus concealed from common view, may be new partly—perhaps entirely; but, however that may be, there is no doubt that the idea of making this use of galvanism did not originate with Mr. Colt; and that its successful application to submarine explosions was made by

others, before Mr. Colt's projects were submitted to the public.

The use under water, of gunpowder, in blasting rocks, levelling for foundations, removing obstructions to navigation, and even blowing up vessels, is a matter of common notoriety amongst persons conversant in such operations. But, until within a few years, fire was communicated in such cases, by matches or fuses of different kinds, through water-tight tubes, &c.; all of which means seem applicable only to charges that are near at hand.

In 1831, however, an eminent American chemist, (Dr. Hare, of Philadelphia,) at the close of a paper describing a process by which he had exploded a number of charges of gunpowder by the use of a galvanic battery, says, "it must be obvious, that, in all cases of blasting under water, the plan of the tin tube, and ignition by a galvanic circuit, must be very eligible."

Although the English have since had much more experience than we in carrying out this idea, they acknowledge this to be the first suggestion of the voltaic process. Since this announcement by Dr. Hare, originality in this matter must be restricted to the details, which admit, no doubt, of considerable variety.

Col. Pasley, of the English corps of engineers, after much experience in submarine explosions by the employment of fuses, matches, &c., began experiments in the autumn of 1838 with the voltaic battery; and, in the spring of 1839, succeeded in firing several charges in deep water, at the distance of about 500 feet.

In the same year, Mr. Roberts, near Edinburgh, used a voltaic battery in firing charges under water.

In July, 1839, Col. Pasley caused experiments to be made as to the effects of an increased size in the conducting wire, and augmented power in the battery in exploding more remote deposites of powder, in which he extended the distance to 1,950 feet—a limit set, not by want of power in the apparatus, not by defect in the arrangements, but by the length of wire with which he was provided. There was nothing in the experiments then made, nor is there anything in those made since, affording any reason to doubt that, had his provision of wire been adequate, he might, at that time, have extended his command over a length of wire as great as has ever been employed.

"As soon as Col. Pasley" (to use the language of a semi-official report of these proceedings, dated in 1840) "was satisfied that he could depend upon the voltaic battery at any depth of water, and in any current however strong," he made arrangements for blowing to pieces the wreck of the line-of-battle ship Royal George, sunk at Spithead in 1782, and then lying embedded in mud at a depth of about fourteen fathoms; which operation was pursued through several seasons. Numerous embarrassments connected with the position of the wreck in deep water, in a strong tide way, and often a rough and heavy sea, attended the early operations; but they were all overcome, and the process reduced to a system simple, easy and certain.

In December, 1839, the wreck of the barque Equitable, of 420 tons, was blown up in 30 feet water in the river Hoogly, in India—also by voltaic electricity.

In the year 1840, Mr. Alexander Paris, an able American

civil engineer, who was engaged, under the general government, in the construction of quay walls and launching ways at the navy-yard in Portsmouth, N.H., had recourse, with perfect success, to the same agent in levelling the rocky bottom to receive his walls, in depths varying from 25 to 30 feet at high water. He preferred, for his galvanic battery, Dr. Hare's calorimeter [calorimotor].

With this experience, (which we see has been acquired by others than Mr. Colt,) with much more of similar nature to which I have not adverted, and a vast deal more, no doubt, of which I have no information; for, in the development of this branch of chemical philosophy, great improvements are daily made in the details, in sources of power, in modes and purposes of application,—with this knowledge, any intelligent person could, I have no doubt, aided by equal munificence, without invading any patent, and by merely applying means which have been gratuitously contributed to the cause of science, accomplish all that Mr. Colt has achieved. I do not say that he would use the same means identically, because the same effects may be reached by processes varying in particulars; but he would accomplish the same end with equal certainty, although what Mr. Colt claims as the secret of his process should never transpire.

I should consider myself as risking nothing were I to engage to have these results repeated, without the least reference to Mr. Colt's—using only processes that are now the property of the scientific world—with modifications probably, but with such only as ingenuity, by no means rare, could supply.

Even within the short time that has elapsed since Col. Pasley and Mr. Paris's experiments, and other above adverted to, the galvanic battery has been greatly extended in its power and convenience of application; but by means openly announced to the public, and better than which Mr. Colt need not have used in his late exhibitions.

To meet the probability of its being said that, after all, the agent is not galvanism,—I have to add, that galvanism will, at any rate, produce identical effects. If it be further said, that the explosions are not the work of gunpowder,— it is only necessary to add, that pyrotechnical displays not less striking, may, nevertheless, be the work of that material.

II. *Whether the mode of the application of this agent to harbor defence be new?*

I am not aware of any project antecedent to Mr. Colt's, for communicating fire by galvanic electricity to deposites of powder placed in channels and harbors, for their defence. If, however, it were once thought advisable to make these deposites, it would seem that this mode of igniting them— a mode which has been shown to have been of frequent use in causing explosions under water for other purposes— would very naturally have been taken into consideration; but, I must say, I am not aware of any such project.

If the purpose of the resolution is (without confining its meaning to the mere process of ignition) to inquire whether the idea of defending harbors by such deposites of gunpowder placed in the track of the vessels is new, then the answer is in the negative; Fulton's projects of this sort are more than 40 years old. Among his various devices for producing submarine explosions, and for attaching torpedoes,

as he called them, to the bottom of vessels, was one (perhaps the best of all such inventions) for anchoring one or more lines of torpedoes across the channel, and below the surface of the water, and in such proximity to each other that vessels could not pass without striking one or more. Each of these magazines of powder was to be so fitted on the outside, that the pressure of passing bodies would set free an internal lock, like a gun lock, thereby giving fire to the enclosed gunpowder. This invention, the details of which afford scope for much variety, seems to me more likely to be usefully applied to purposes of defence, and much freer from objections, than any kindred project. The idea has long been before the world, to be availed of, possibly, in particular localities, in addition to other well-tried means, when suitable occasions shall present themselves.

With Mr. Fulton's other device of detached torpedoes, that were to be drifted down upon anchored vessels— although, in his preliminary experiments in the harbor of New York, he had completely demolished the vessel submitted to his power—one or two actual attacks that were attempted during the last war, produced no other effect than causing a more than usual vigilance in the blockading vessels. This particular invention of drifting torpedoes, notwithstanding the striking success of the experiment in the presence of thousands of spectators, never partook of the public confidence, and received little further aid from the government.

These notices but repeat the well-known fact, that submarine explosions are not new resorts as measures of defence, in the minds of ingenious men; however it may be with Mr. Colt's means of causing the explosion.

III. *If new, what objections there are against its adoption, if objections do exist?*

Means as applicable to the great object of national defence may be local or particular, or they may be general. Of the former class, it would be difficult to mention any means that can be brought to inflict bodily hurt upon man, or injury upon the works of his hands, that may not find some useful application in war.

We pride ourselves in these days (and not without reason) upon the highly advanced state of military science; upon the great exactitude to which its combinations lead; the precision of its results, whether in respect to masses or individuals; upon the perfection of its machinery and its arms; and yet, indispensable as this advanced condition is, in order that one nation may be in equilibrium with another, or may be able promptly to put herself upon the same level, there would be hardly a day of active campaign in which advantageous recourse would not be had to some of the simple practices of early warfare. The bayonet is not, however, likely to be set aside, because in a *mêlée,* the fist may be sometimes used with effect even now; nor the musket, because in certain positions the arrow may be the preferable missile. But, while particular circumstances of this nature do undoubtably sometimes arise, no judicious person would therefore decry the great improvements that have grown out of the experience of war, or aim to supersede any of these by devices not approved by an equally severe test. Military experience has enacted, as an inflexible law, that no device, however plausible, shall be admitted to confidence as a military resource, except as it shall make its way by success in actual war, or in a long and severe course of experience analogous thereto. The success of any device as a local or particular means, ought, in this way, to be thoroughly established, before it can enter its claim as of general utility. And the reason for this is plain: as the means in actual use are the fruits of this kind of experience, they should give way only to means that have been proved superior, by a trial not less thorough.

These observations seem properly to precede the remark that the project of defending harbors by deposites of gunpowder arranged for blowing up the passing vessels of an enemy, is very far from possessing the sanctions which alone could warrant a reliance upon it, to the exclusion of a single one of the means of known efficiency.

Still, it might be conceded that, in certain positions, and under particular circumstances, a partial resort to it might be advantageous. I can imagine a case that would call for the use of Perkins's steam-gun—an invention which excited the public wonder a few years ago—in preference to any other arm; and I can also conceive circumstances that would justify the trial of *this* project. But even were any such case to present itself, the object could be accomplished without recourse to any secret means—to any process not the common property of the world. I must add, however, that even in instances that would seem to admit this latter trial, any arrangement founded on the principle of Mr. Fulton's anchored torpedoes, presents itself much more favorably to my mind.

To apply this project as of general use, or as a sole resort, would, it seems to me, be as utterly in vain as it would be unwise. In order to explode these gunpowder deposites opportunely, it is, of course, necessary that the agent shall know, with exactness, when the passing vessel is over the charge—very little latitude being allowable. Now, the only mode of judging is by the eye; there is no time for computation, nor even for comparison of opinions; and to say that a man can guess within several hundred feet, is to give more accurate vision than the most experienced eye would claim. In proof of this, it is only necessary to compare the opinions of bystanders as to the distance of any remote object, whether passing by land or water. In order that there may be any approach to accuracy in this respect, it is necessary, moreover, that the agent shall be placed in, or near, the line in which his magazines lie; if not, he can no better decide when the enemy is crossing this line, than he can tell the particular point of the line over which he passes. But if there be, unavoidably, this uncertainty by daylight, how will it be at night, when the outline of the vessel can only be dimly made out, if seen at all? How is this resort then to be applied?

Passing from this point, as to which many sources of uncertainty are obvious, we will suppose an enemy to hesitate, notwithstanding, as to running the hazard of the passage—preferring to land a force, and break up the arrangement for communicating fire to charges of powder. The success of this landing can be prevented in one of two ways only. There must be a fortification and garrison capable of resisting the enterprise—which we know, from the lessons

of history, will be composed of a force commensurate with the importance of the object to be gained; or, there must be encamped upon the spot an army capable of defeating it without the aid of fortifications. The defence rests, then, either upon the fort or upon the army, and not upon the deposites of powder; for, if this protecting force be overcome, there will then remain nothing to prevent the breaking up and destruction of the galvanic arrangements. Or the enemy may prefer to destroy the system of conducting wires as they lie upon the bottom. For this purpose, he may send at night his heavy boats—aided, perhaps, by one or two small steamboats, each provided with the means of dragging the bottom, so as to break the wires, and tear away the powder cases. Traversing the channel in all directions within the scope of the deposites, a single night would suffice to clear away from the portion of the channel designed to be followed, every trace of submarine communication. Nor would the use of hawsers, or even chains, intended to secure the wires from the dredges, avail; because, with means supplied by the larger boats of men-of-war, these could be lifted and cut off.

On the supposition that this is to be the main dependence for defence, there would, however, be no necessity for hurry in this dredging operation; the enemy might take his own time to it. Bringing his vessels of war into convenient proximity, he could delay his passage until a deliberate examination had shown that not a clew remained unbroken.

It must not be urged that danger to the boats will prevent the scouring of the bottom; because to say nothing of the uncertainty which must exist on shore as to the exact positions of the boats at any moment in the night, we know that greater hazards are encountered in war with alacrity. A little additional pay to the soldier, and the thirst for distinction in the officer, keep the military miners stimulated for weeks, during a siege, to willing and ardent labors, in the midst of almost hourly explosions.

Nor must it be assumed that the positions occupied by these means of defence will be unknown to an enemy. If these were not settled by the features of the harbor, money would procure this, as it does all other military information. If the dark and complicated countermine galleries of a fortification cannot remain unknown, we need not look for the concealment of that which must be executed in the face of the public.

I could enlarge on these and other considerations of a like nature, explaining counter-devices, by which the project, standing by itself, would be rendered nugatory; but such cannot be necessary, and I will sum up my remarks in the following words:

That the project of Mr. Colt, as a sole means of defence, is wholly undeserving of consideration; as an auxiliary, although it might in some situations be resorted to, it should in all, or nearly all such cases, be regarded as inferior to means that have long been known; and, even when resorted to, that it may be applied without any indebtedness to Mr. Colt, either as an inventor, an improver, or an applier of the process.

Mr. Colt declines affording you the explanations and information respecting his process, which you invited him to communicate. This circumstance does not, however, affect the tenor of this report. As before observed, although we should forever remain ignorant of the mode of operation preferred by him, the results he has given to the public can be repeated by others whenever they may be called for.

I have the honor to be, very respectfully, your most obedient,

Jos. G. Totten,
Colonel and Chief Engineer.

Hon. Wm. Wilkins,
Secretary of War.

APPENDIX 8: Letter of Professor Joseph Henry to Secretary of War William Wilkins, 3 May 1844, in *Colt's Submarine Battery*, House Document No. 127, 28th Congress, 2nd Session, page 16–17. [Henry's retained copy, with very minor variations, is found in the Joseph Henry Papers, Smithsonian Institution Archives, Washington, D.C.]

Princeton College, N.J. May 3, 1844.

Sir: I have the honor to acknowledge the receipt of a letter from the War Department, requesting my views as to the originality of Mr. Colt's method of producing explosions; it being understood, according to your statement, that the combustible he employs is gunpowder, and that this is fired by means of galvanism, or other similar agency. In answer to this letter, I respectfully submit the following:

The explosion of gunpowder at a distance, by means of galvanism, has been familiar to men of science and practical engineers for several years. The method now generally used was made public in 1832, and is the invention of Dr. Hare, of Philadelphia. It consists, essentially, in extending between the reservoir of powder and the operator two long thick wires of copper, the further ends of which, terminating in the powder, are united by a short wire of platinum of small diameter. The other ends of the copper wires, in the hands of the operator, at the desired moment of explosion being suddenly brought into contact with the two poles of a galvanic battery, a current of galvanism is transmitted through the circuit of wires, which, heating to redness the piece of platinum in the midst of the powder, produces the explosion.

The practicability of exploding gunpowder at a distance, in this way, was established by the experiments of Dr. Hare; and his results were verified and applied to actual practice by several persons, before the time of the exhibitions of Mr. Colt. In 1839, a series of experiments by Colonel Pasley, of the royal engineers, was published in England, relative to the explosion of a large quantity of powder by the galvanic process, at the bottom of the river Medway; and, as an evidence of the wide diffusion of the knowledge of this process, I may mention, that I have now before me a book published in Calcutta, in 1841, in which is given a minute account of the experiments of Dr. O'Shaughnessy, of the Bengal army, in destroying a wreck sunk in Hoogly river,

by a method which the author himself calls the process of Dr. Hare.

The experiments on the Hoogly, as well as these on the Medway, were made in 1839; and since that time, as it would appear by the various publications on the subject in the different English scientific journals, the application of the galvanic process of exploding gunpowder has become an established part of the business of the English engineer. In short, I consider the laws of the transmission of electricity through long wires as fully developed by the researches of Ohm, Wheatstone, Daniell, and others,—at least as far as they are applicable to the process in question; that I do not think it in the least degree probable that Mr. Colt has added a single essential fact to the previously existing stock of knowledge on this subject.

In conclusion, I wish it to be distinctly understood that the foregoing remarks are all made in reference to the method of exploding gunpowder at a distance by means of galvanism, and are intended as a specific answer to the question proposed to me in your letter. Mr. Colt may, perhaps, not attempt to found his claims to originality on the invention of the galvanic process, to which he can have no title, but on a new application of this process to a method of harbor defence; and also on a new arrangement of subaqueous magazines for the same purpose. Of the validity of claims thus founded, I am not called on to give my opinion; but, in justice to Mr. Colt, I ought to say, that whatever may be the result of the investigations relative to the originality of his plans, I think he deserves credit for the industry and practical skill with which he has brought them before the public.

I have the honor to be, very respectfully, your obedient servant,

JOSEPH HENRY.

Hon. Wm. Wilkins,
Secretary of War.

APPENDIX 9: Letter of Thomas P. Jones to Secretary of War William Wilkins, 7 May 1844, in *Colt's Submarine Battery*, House Document No. 127, 28th Congress, 2nd Session, page 17.

Washington, May 7, 1844

Sir: I have carefully perused the communication from Professor Hare, which you placed in my hands, and do not think it necessary to add anything to the remarks of that gentleman. The view he takes of the subject to which it relates, is precisely that which had presented itself to my mind; and the authorities which he has adduced, being principally found on the pages of my journal, are such as I should have immediately resorted to. Dr. Hare has done me the honor of referring you to me, should you desire any information in addition to that which his communication affords. I cannot pretend, by anything I can say, to add weight to his statements; but he is aware that I am perfectly [acquainted] with his agency in perfecting the plan for effecting the explosion of powder in blasting rocks, and for other purposes, by means of galvanic electricity; which plan, slightly modified, is that which has been successfully adopted.

Mr. Colt may have made some new modification of the conducting wires, or in some other parts of the apparatus used by him; but this is a question of little importance, as every person well acquainted with chemistry and mechanical philosophy, and who is apt at manipulation, could very readily accomplish all that has been effected by that gentleman, and without liability to failure. There are hundreds of men of science in our country, who would unhesitatingly engage so to do. Without consulting with these gentlemen, I may, with confidence, refer you to Professors B.F. [sic] Morse, A.D. Bache, C.G. Page, and W.R. Johnson, now in this city, as I am certain that they will unite in confirming these statements.

I am, sir, very respectfully, your obedient servant,

THOS. P. JONES.

Hon. WM. WILKINS,
Secretary of War.

APPENDIX 10: Letter of Secretary of the Navy John Y. Mason to Secretary of War William Wilkins, 7 May 1844, in *Colt's Submarine Battery*, House Document No. 127, 28th Congress, 2nd Session, page 5.

Navy Department, May 7, 1844.

SIR: I have received your letter of this date, informing me that you are engaged in the preparation of a report on the subject of Colt's submarine battery.

It appears that there has been paid, under orders from this department, to Mr. Colt, and to his order, by virtue of the joint resolution of August 31, 1842, up to the 22nd of November, 1843, the sum of $15,050.62; and the amount of facilities furnished other than money (excepting some small articles of which no account has been received) is in value $2,353.50. Since the date above referred to, no payment has been made by the department on that account.

I have reason to believe that Mr. Colt did communicate to the Hon. A.P. Upshur information as to the combustible agent employed by him in his experiments, while that gentleman was the head of this department; that this communication was made under an injunction of secrecy; and there is nothing in existence in this department to show, so far as I am informed, that the secret has been divulged by him, or is applicable to the purposes of the government, without some arrangement with Mr. Colt, which this department has no authority to make.

As Mr. Colt's experiments were, in effect, closed about the time I entered on the duties of this office, I have declined to receive a communication of Mr. Colt's secret, of which the knowledge could only be useful in determining on the effect of experiments which had already been made, which I had not witnessed, and which there was no means at the disposal of the department to have repeated.

I have the honor to be, very respectfully, your obedient servant,

J.Y. MASON.

Hon. WM. WILKINS,
Secretary of War.

APPENDIX 11: Letter of Secretary of War William Wilkins to the Honorable J. W. Jones, Speaker of the House of Representatives, 8 May 1844, in *Colt's Submarine Battery*, House Document No. 127, 28th Congress, 2nd Session, pages 1–3.

War Department, May 8, 1844.

SIR: I have the honor to acknowledge the receipt of a copy of the resolution adopted by the House of Representatives on the 19th of the last month, directing the Secretaries of War and the Navy "to communicate the fact, whether the combustible agent used by Mr. Colt was a secret before he made the same known at the seat of government, and whether the mode of its application to harbor defence be new; and, if new, what objections there are to its adoption, if objections do exist."

The subjects embraced by this resolution, and submitted to the consideration of this department, necessarily occasioned an examination and inquiries productive of the delay which has occurred in rendering the required report.

Public attention has been directed, for some time, to the experiments of Mr. Colt, and it is presumed that the nature of the agents which he employs is well understood. As no special communication, such as is supposed in the resolution of the House, had been made to the War Department, with a view to enable Mr. Colt to point out what he considered novel in his means and appliances, I addressed him a letter; the reply to which, with a previous note from him, is hereto appended. It will be perceived, too, by the reply, herewith transmitted, from the honorable the Secretary of the Navy, to my letter addressed to him on the 7th instant, that Mr. Colt has been so guarded and cautious in his communications with that department, as to keep from us all light and explanation as to his combustible agent, and the means of its employment.

For the purpose of being put in possession of the views of the appropriate department in regard to the question of "harbor defence," the resolution was referred for report to Colonel Totten, the able chief of the corps of engineers. His full and lucid reply, examined and sanctioned by the experienced and scientific officers at the head of the Topographical and Ordnance Bureaus, is hereto appended.

With a desire, also, to bring the judgment of men of general science to bear upon the subject, and especially to obtain their opinions and facts in reference to the alleged "secret," and pretended originality of invention by Mr. Colt, I addressed letters, covering copies of the resolution of the House, to Professors Hare, of Philadelphia, and Henry, of Princeton. Their replies, as well as a letter from Dr. Thomas

P. Jones, of Washington, referring to Professor Hare's communication, are hereto annexed.

The protest of Mr. Colt, to be found in his letter addressed to me on the 22nd ultimo, and his suggestions as to the reply to be made by this department, I have, of course, under a view of the resolution of the House, felt it my duty to disregard.

It is generally understood that gunpowder is the explosive agent used by Mr. Colt, and that galvanism is employed to fire it; that harbors are to be defended by deposites of gunpowder fired at will, and at a distance, by the aid of galvanism. In regard to the use of these means, the communications just referred to establish conclusively the following points:

1st. That as respects the employment of a galvanic current to ignite a wire, and, by that means, to fire simultaneously numerous charges of gunpowder, it was applied by that distinguished professor, Dr. Hare, of Philadelphia, as early as 1833, to rock-blasting, and proposed as a means of defence.

2d. The idea of making this use of galvanism did not originate with Mr. Colt; and its successful application to submarine explosions was made by Colonel Pasley, Mr. Roberts, Mr. Paris, and others, before Mr. Colt's projects were submitted to the public.

3d. That the suggestion to apply to harbor defence deposites of gunpowder, to be fired by galvanism, flows so naturally from the use of that agent in producing submarine explosions at a distance, that no novelty can be assumed for the idea; and that it is, in fact, merely an application of the agent, galvanism, to fire Fulton's stationary torpedoes. The proposal to defend harbors by deposites of gunpowder is not novel, nor is it novel to fire such deposites beneath the water by galvanism.

4th. That even if novelty could be claimed for this mode of harbor defence, it is liable to fatal objections as a primary means of that object; and as an auxiliary means, to very strong objections. The precise position of a vessel, by day and night, cannot be ascertained by the operator who controls the galvanic battery, so as to produce the explosion at the moment when it will be effective. The arrangement of the wires for transmitting the galvanic current may easily be destroyed. The operator must be protected by a fortification, or by an army, to prevent the destruction of all his means of action by the landing of the enemy. And, whilst upon this point, I may remark, that the very supposition (as stated in Colonel Totten's report) of danger to the boats of the enemy, tends to prove the security of their fleet; for, if the magazines were exploded in order to destroy the boats employed in search of the wires, then the fleet would be without cause of fear, and the harbor without defence. The hazard of those boats employed in the search would not be equal to the *"forlorn hope"* in storming a fortified place, and would, like that, be a regular military duty. But the unprofitableness of blowing up the boats employed in the search would, of itself, make the search a safe duty, and therefore the communications with the magazines would always be found, and the duty of searching for them would be without hazard. Yet, admitting the risk, by special arrangements for that purpose, it is no more than that of a *"forlorn hope,"* and is over with the first boat exposed to

it. Other boats can then complete the search, and the destruction of the connecting wires, at leisure, and with impunity.

5th. If the means assumed to be those employed by Mr. Colt (and if we are in error, he has his own caution alone to blame) are actually not those which he uses, then I affirm that any intelligent, scientific person, aided and encouraged by equal munificence and appropriations, could, without invading any patent or exclusive right of others, and by merely applying means which have been gratuitously contributed to science by distinguished men of our country, accomplish all that Mr. Colt has achieved under the bounty and generous encouragement of his government, in his peaceful experiments against a defenseless and untenanted ship.

Whatever may be the claim to merit, on account of the skill and handiwork of Mr. Colt, displayed in his preparations and uninterrupted experiments on the shores of the Potomac, it will probably be acquiesced in by all, that if the expenditure of seventeen thousand four hundred and four dollars and twelve cents ($17,404.12) does not impair that claim to merit, it will, at all events, be considered as a generous encouragement to the exercise of his talents.

I have the honor to be, sir, with high respect, your obedient servant,

WM. WILKINS,
Secretary of War.

Hon. J.W. JONES,
Speaker of the House of Representatives.

APPENDIX 12: Letter of Samuel Colt to the Honorable Henry C. Murphy, Committee on Naval Affairs, House of Representatives, 3 June 1844, at Washington City, retained copy, Samuel Colt Papers, box 6, Connecticut Historical Society, Hartford.

Washington City June 3rd 1844

Sir

Agreeable to your wish I give below the history of my inventions for harbour defence and the motives and inducement which have prompted me in submitting the same for the patronage and use of our Govt. together with what I consider the advantage to be derived from its use.

The idea of submarine explosions for purposes of Harbour defence was concieved by me as early as the year 1829 while stud[y]ing in the laboratory of a bleeching and colouring establishment at Ware Vilage [,] Massachusetts, and I made sundry experiments in a small scale at that time and repeated them in various ways for several successive years thereafter.

In the spring of 1836 I returned hastily from Europe to this Country in company with our charge d'Affaires to the Court of France in consequence of the threatening aspect of affairs, growing out of our French relations. Before I left Paris every thing seemed to render a war eventable [inevitable] with the French, and my desire was to aid my own Government in the struggle, by placing at their disposal my own services with the plans and inventions I had made in repeating Fire Arms, projectiles, water proof cartridges, and my submarine fortifications. It so happened that I had scarcely reached Washington before a settlement of our difficulties with France was peacably effected, and finding there was like to be no immediate call for my inventions in submarine fortifications, I determined not to make my secrets known until I had the *means* to more completely test my plans of operation, and believing the same could be quickest obtained by bringing my repeating Fire arms into Market for the use of the Army operating in Florida & for private sale I employed my time in erecting an armory and getting up Machinery for that object. This being through with and my time again my own I revived my study and experiments to perfect my plans for harbour defence.

In the spring of 1841 War again threatened our Country, growing out of the disputed boundary of the state of Maine. The importance of my invention presented itself to my mind with more force that ever and then for the first time I made a communication to our Government on the subject. My communication, to the President of the U. States, was accompanied by letters from the Honorable Samuel L. Southard [,] President of the U. States Senate and one from Major Genl William Gibbs McNeill late of the Corps of U. States Topographical Engineers. To these gentlemen I confidentially communicated the whole secrets of my Invention, and they fully sustained me in my projects. The matter was referred to the Honorable George E. Badger [(]then Secretary of the Navy) who on examining my propositions to prove by an exhibition at my own expense the utility of my plans [,] Determined that the Department had no power to enter into the contract proposed by me, but expressed his willingness that I should make the proposed exhibition at the expense of the Government[. I] promised I would make such exposure of my plans to him in *confidence* as would satisfy him that the project was plausable and he promised when tried [if] it should prove successful, the Government would reward me for the full value of my secrets. I acceeded to these terms and went into explanation of the whole matter to him. The result was that he conferred with the President of the U. States and the chairman of the Navy Committees of Congress and a resolution was passed which authorized the expenditure of $50,000 in experiments. It was deemed expedient to keep my name out of the bill making this approbation [appropriation] but that said appropriation was made with *"special reference"* to my projects. I refer you for confirmation to a letter from the Honorable Secretary of the Navy dated July 20, 1841, to the Honorable President of the U. S. Senate, a copy of which was sent to me at the time and it induced me to commence preperations for my submarine Exhibition on the scale contemplated. Soon after the passage of this bill a change in the Cabinet occurred, and the Honorable Mr. Upshur succeeded Mr. Badger at the head of the Navy Department. I did not expect that any change would be made by Mr. Upshur in the plans just agreed upon for the proposed exhibition and I persuaded [pursued] my experiments without communicating with the new Secretary until it became necessary to pay some of the bills accumulating in progress of my work. By the request of Mr. Upshur I then came to Washington and went over with him the whole

plans and secrets of my inventions which so far convinced him of their practicability that to remove the only remaining doubt he simply required me to make the single experiment of the blowing up of a vessel at a distance beyond the reach of an enemy's shot, to satisfy him of the full adoptation [adaptability] of my plans for the purposes intended. I accordingly prepared for an exhibition in the Potomac River and [a] blow up of a small vessel anchored off the U.S. Arsenal from a point on the river near Alexandria five miles distant. The complete success of this experiment so entirely satisfied the Secretary of the Navy that my project must succeed and he wrote a note to the Chairman of the Navy Committee setting forth his entire satisfaction at the result and desire if any further tests were wanted to prove its efficiency for the satisfaction of Congress that an expression of Congress to that effect should be made. Accordingly the joint resolution under which I have been making my recent experiments and exhibitions in the East branch of the Potomac was passed [by] Congress. In preparing for which I fortified the Potomac River so completely that no enemy's vessel, or fleet that could enter its mouth could reach the Navy Yard without being one and all destroyed. My drafts on the Government to pay for all my preliminary experiments and this fortification [,] together with even the purchasing of the ship on which the experiments was made, and the final removal of her sunken wreck from the bed of the river [,] has only been $15,877.27, of which $15,050.62 have been paid by the Navy Department out of the appropriation of $50,000 procured for experiments with my Submarine Battery. The temporary fortification which I made with this means if prepared before hand could have been located in the Potomac River in one night and an enemy's force larger than that which *once burnt the city of Washington* could be destroyed in its passage either up, or down the River, without discovering any signs of its danger or having the power of resistance when operated upon. A fisherman's houses, or barn, or even the top of a tree, any where within five miles distance could be made the position from which the engineer would operate on the enemy.

Fortifications of my construction can be made either permanent or portable as necessity require and may be so contrived that in either case they can be operated without any material increase of expense by from one to one hundred or any greater number of men stationed in as many different places at any reasonable distance from the seen [scene] of action and the cutting of [off] or capture of any one, or all but one of them and that one may be either one of them, would not weaken our command over the whole fortifications prepared for the destruction of the enemy. In my original letter to the President of the United States I offered to show that a harbour like that of New York could be fortified at an expense less than the cost of a steamship of War, and when once prepared [,] a few engineers alone were sufficient to operate it against any fleet Europe could send. The resolution originally introduced by the Chairman of the Military Committee provided that should I succeed in accomplishing what I were called upon to perform them [then] I were to be employed to fortify on my plan whatever harbour should be selected for that purpose provided I would undertake the same at a cost not exceeding that of the average cost of the

U. States steamships Missouri & Mississippi. The Resolution as thus introduced was referred to the Committee on Naval Affairs and by my own consent the last class [clause] of the bill was struck off to wait the result of the experiments then contemplated before the same should be acted upon. *My wish now is* either to carry into execution my plans for a permanent submarine fortification to supercede those that have been & are to be built in N. York Harbour, for which there have been already expended plans and estimates made amounting in cost without their armaments or stores to $6,454,984. or to fortify any other harbour selected for that purpose. I could attend at the same time to any surveys and examination going on under the direction of the Navy Department of those harbours and Rivers where new fortifications are deemed necessary and are contemplated soon to be made with a view to make estimates and ascertain their adoption [adaptability] to this peculiar mode of fortification as an auxiliary to or substitute for those contemplated of common construction. Also to commence the manufacture of the materials requisite for portable fortifications for the defence of any rivers or passes in case of sudden immergency.

The number of men in a war establish[ment] requisite to man the forts that have been and are to be built for the defence of N. York according to reports from the War Department is 10,250, which estimate the whole expense of each soldier at half that of a mounted dragoon ($1000 a year) would cost the Government annually $5,128,000 as [a] sum which in a few years would fortify the cost [coast] from New Brunswick to Mexico, with my Submarine Batteries. It may be argued by those interested in building and arming *Bricks & water forts* that an enemy could either operate from boats or by landing on the rough beach at a distance, cut of [off] my engineers or their multiplicity of means to operate my Batteries.

I would answer these suggestions by saying it is reasonable to suppose that if I can blow up a hundred ships, I can be in a condition to meet the *attack* of as many row boats as such a fleet can send without weakening my means of defence against the ships themselves, but to admit for the sake of argument that the enemy could operate unmolested in boats [,] they never could know when their task was completed (and they must be pulling up "decoy duck" or the trigers to their own distruction). This is not the case with fortifications of common construction for when they are once captured the enemy is out of danger, and if a force is to land on the beach to capture my fortifications from behind [,] can they not do the same in the case of common fortifications. Again, if an enemy can land on the beach and march an army over our Country with impunity [,] where is the use of fortification of any discriptions.

It must appear then to every sane and unprejudiced mind, that wherever fortifications are built or to be built on our cost [coast], they are intended to protect our harbours and rivers against the entrance of an enemy's ships and if the Government continue to appropriate millions annually for its cost [coastal] defence [,] would it not be better to use that money or a portion of it in a way to secure the protection of the greatest possible extent of our cost [coast].

In presenting my claim on the Government for a fulfilment of their promise to give me a "reward adequate to my invention," I wish to have it to be distinctly understood that I never have from the commencement of my experiments, neither do I now pretend that I am the inventor of any peculiar combustible substance to be employed in my explosions, nor should I do so even if I had contrived any better than many that are well known which will answer that purpose.

Gunpowder has been long known and well known and its first employment for submarine explosions to destroy ships is due to Robert Fulton. The powers of electricity to ignite gunpowder has also been long known and to Franklin is due the credit of first employing that fluid for useful purpose. Galvanic Electricity is equally well known at the present day and to one of our distinguished countrymen Dr. Robert Hare of Phila. is no doubt due the credit of employing that means for useful purpose in blasting rocks either blow [below] or above water, and the idea of removing sunken rocks [wrecks] (The Royal George for example) and recovering treasure from the bottom of the sea by employing that agent, to communicate fire to explosive substances has undoubtedly originated from hints given by publications from the pen of that Gentleman, and I am proud to be able to trace back so much of the means that can aid in making a submarine battery to American oregon [origin], yet these things in the primative state do not make a submarine battery for fortifying a harbour against an advancing squadron, and if these agencies in any form are now used by me (who first concieved the idea of such submarine fortification) it does not follow that there are not means unknown to the public, that could not be used to produce the same effect at the time the idea first suggested itself to my mind. *I claim to be the originator of a submarine battery with peculiarities which has enabled me to perform what has never before been accomplished* and on a full explanation of my plans and secrets to my Government, *originality* of plans was not only admitted but I were encouraged to prove in practice what seemed plausable in my theory, and I were to have if successful a reward adequate to the advantage to be derived therefrom[.] *I have proven every thing contemplated or regarding which a doubt was entertained,* and now I desire the further action of Government on my claims to their promise "quid propo" [*quid pro quo*].

> I have the honor to be very
> respectfully, Sir, yr Obt Servt
> Saml Colt.

APPENDIX 13: Patent petition for Samuel Colt's Submarine Battery, 8 June 1844, Samuel Colt Papers, box 6, Connecticut Historical Society, Hartford.

To all whom it may concern, be it known, that I Samuel Colt of the City of New York in the State of New York, have invented a new and useful mode of using amunition for Military purposes, and more particularly for the using of gunpowder to make submarine explosions in such manner as to destroy vessels when under sail in harbors or channels, and I do hereby declare that the following is a full and exact description thereof.

I prepare a number of metallic or other vessels for containing powder, and within the body of the powder contained in such vessel I insert a platinum, or other suitable wire, which may be ignited by means of a current of the Electric fluid passed through it from a Galvanic Battery, or other instrument adapted to that purpose, the connecting wires, and other arrangements, being such as are well known to men of science conversant with chemistry and mechanical philosophy. To the vessel containing the powder I will, for the sake of description, apply the name of Torpedo. These I anchor, or otherwise dispose of in the channel where vessels must pass. In the drawing No. 1, A,A, may represent two of these torpedoes; and A,A,A, in sheet No. 2 represents a channel studded with them over the whole width. In this drawing B, may represent the station of the battery, or instrument for supplying the electric current, this station is represented as in the vicinity of the channel where the torpedoes are placed, and this may, in general be so situated; but the apparatus may be so arranged as for the operator to be at a very considerable distance from the channel through which vessels are expected to pass.

A main point in the producing of submarine explosions, so as to destroy a vessel under sail is to ascertain the instant when such vessel is directly over one of the torpedoes, and this I effect in two ways, in one of which it is ascertained by reflection, by means of mirrors, which can be managed by one observer. In the other it is ascertained by the concurrent observation of two persons, so situated as they may observe a vessel from two points of view, and that when the vessel has arrived at the angular point formed by the two lines of observation, the concurrent action of the observers shall cause a torpedo to explode at that point.

In drawing No. 3, I have given a sketch of the manner in which the place of a vessel is ascertained by reflection. C, is a convex mirror so situated as to take in the whole field of view of the channel, or harbour where the torpedoes are anchored; from this mirror the vessel which may come within the field of view will be reflected, at an angle due to its situation, onto a metallic, or other, mirror, situated at D. This second mirror is surrounded by a number of pieces of metal a,a,a, which constitute the terminations of as many connecting wires as there are torpedoes anchored, and the mirror is so arranged as to exhibit distinctly the place of the reflected image of the vessel, and the connecting wire corresponding with this situation. E, is the Battery, and F,F, the connecting wires leading to and from the respective torpedoes. The operator is consequently enabled to complete the circuit at the moment when the vessel is over the torpedo indicated by the reflection.

Drawing No. 4, will serve to illustrate the manner of ascertaining the place of a vessel, and the manner of producing the explosion by the concurrent action of two observers. Let G, represent the part of a channel where vessels must pass, and where torpedoes are anchored; and let H, and I, represent the stations of two different observers. The station at H, may be one where there is an interruption in the circuit of the connecting wires [;] the observer there is to notice when the vessel is in the line of either of the torpedoes, and is to complete the circuit appertaining to that line. The observer at the station I is in like manner to ascertain when the vessel is in the line of either of the torpedoes, and is to make the connexion corresponding therewith. If both observations meet in the same angular point there will be an explosion, and the vessel will be destroyed, but until this concurrence happens neither of the torpedoes will explode.

The whole of the apparatus used for eliciting and conducting the electric current, and for producing ignition in the powder is, as before observed [,] well understood by men of science, and no claim whatever is therefore made to such apparatus, but the combining therewith the two reflectors so as to indicate the moment when a vessel is over one of the torpedoes is altogether new, and is therefore claimed by me as the subject matter of a patent. The combining with such a battery, and with the torpedoes, of the interrupted circuit in the connecting wires, and of the observation and concurrent action of the two observers, on the principle, and in the manner set forth, is also new, and is hereby claimed as making a part of my invention or discovery.

Sam. Colt

Witnesses { Thos P. Jones
           { N Callarifer [?]

APPENDIX 14: Letter of Thomas P. Jones, editor of the *Journal of the Franklin Institute*, to Samuel Colt, 14 June 1844, in *Colt's Submarine Battery*, House Document No. 127, 28th Congress, 2nd Session, page 24 [original in Colt Papers, box 6, Connecticut Historical Society, Hartford].

Washington, June 14, 1844.

Dear Sir: In answer to your inquiry, I have the great pleasure in stating that, having been made acquainted with the manner in which you produce an explosion which will destroy a vessel when under sail, I am well assured that your plan is not only novel, but also calculated to effect the purpose with a certainty nearly unerring.

The principles upon which you proceed may, undoubtedly, be made the subject of a patent, were it desirable to obtain one.

You will readily perceive that the opinion now offered does not in any manner contravene those which were given to the honorable the Secretary of War, in the replies made by several gentlemen of science to his letter of inquiry, as it relates to matters which were not, and could not be, presented to them.

I am, sir, very respectfully, your obedient servant,

Thos. P. Jones.

Samuel Colt, Esq.

Notes to the Text

[1] Among the most useful early treatises on undersea warfare are HENRY L. ABBOT, *The Beginning of Modern Submarine Warfare under Captain-Lieutenant David Bushnell, Sappers and Miners, Army of the Revolution* (Willets Point, New York: Battalion Press, 1881); FRANCIS M. BARBER, *Lectures on Drifting and Automatic Movable Torpedoes, Submarine Guns and Rockets* (Newport, Rhode Island: U.S. Naval Torpedo Station, 1874); JOHN S. BARNES, *Submarine Warfare, Offensive and Defensive, Including a Discussion of the Offensive Torpedo System, Its Effects upon Iron-Clad Ship Systems, and Influence upon Future Naval Wars* (New York: D. Van Nostrand and Co., 1869); ALAN H. BURGOYNE, *Submarine Navigation, Past and Present,* 2 volumes (London: Richards, 1903); FRIEDRICH VON EHRENKROOK, *Geschichte der Seeminen und Torpedoes* (Berlin: E.S. Mittler und Sohn, 1878); FERNAND FOREST and HENRI NOALHAT, *Les Bateaux Sous-Marines,* 2 volumes (Paris: Ch. Gunod, 1900); EUGÈNE HENNEBERT, *Les Torpilles* (Paris: Librairie Hachette, 1888); HENRI NOALHAT, *Les Torpilles et les mines sous-marines* (Paris: Berger-Levrault et Cie., 1905); CHARLES W. SLEEMAN, *Torpedoes and Torpedo Warfare* (Portsmouth: J. Griffin and Co., 1880); RICHARD H. STOTHERD, *Notes on Torpedoes, Offensive and Defensive* (Washington: Government Printing Office, 1872); and MURRAY F. SUETER, *The Evolution of the Submarine Boat, Mine and Torpedo, from the Sixteenth Century to the Present Time* (Portsmouth: J. Griffin and Co., 1907).

[2] See BERNARD BRODIE, *Sea Power in the Machine Age* (Princeton: Princeton University Press, 1941); J. S. COWIE, *Mines, Minelayers and Minelaying* (London: Oxford University Press, 1949); ROBERT C. DUNCAN, *America's Use of Sea Mines* (Silver Spring, Maryland: U.S. Naval Ordnance Laboratory, 1962); A. M. LOW, *Mine and Countermine* (New York: Sheridan House, 1940); A. A. SAMAROV and F.A. PETROV, editors, *Razvitie minnogo oruzhiya v russkom flote: Dokumenty* [The Development of Mine Materiel in the Russian Navy: Documents] (Moscow: Voenno-morskoe izadatel'stvo voenno-morskogo ministerstva soiuza SSSR, 1951); and G. M. TRUSOV, *Podvodnye lodki v russkom i sovetskom flote* [Submarines in the Russian and Soviet Fleets] (Leningrad: Gosudarstvennoe-soiuznoe izdatel'stvo sudostroitelnoe promyslennosti, 1963).

[3] LEONARD W. LABABEE, editor, *The Papers of Benjamin Franklin,* multivolume edition (New Haven: Yale University Press, 1961 to date), volume 4, pages 145, 202, and volume 10, pages 48, 112n; A. PICARDAT, *Les Mines dans la guerre de campagne* (Paris: Gauthier-Villars, 1874), page 8.

[4] FREDERICK WAGNER, *Submarine Fighter of the American Revolution: The Story of David Bushnell* (New York: Dodd, Mead and Co., 1963), pages 35–45; DAVID BUSHNELL,

"General Principles and Construction of a Submarine Vessel," *Transactions of the American Philosophical Society,* volume 4 (1799), pages 303–312; CARL VAN DOREN, *Benjamin Franklin* (New York: Viking Press, 1938), pages 162–171, 536.

[5] Ibid., pages 563–564; WAGNER, *Bushnell,* pages 52–89, 128 [note 4].

[6] FRANCESCO MASSARDI and others, *Epistolario di Alessandro Volta,* 5 volumes (Bologna: Nicola Zanichelli, 1949–1955), volume 1, pages 162–164, 174–175; BERN DIBNER, *Alessandro Volta and the Electric Battery* (New York: Franklin Watts, 1964), pages 17–39, 64–69, 75–79; I. BERNARD COHEN, editor, *Benjamin Franklin's Experiments: A New Edition of Franklin's "Experiments and Observations on Electricity"* (Cambridge: Harvard University Press, 1941), pages 78–100, 134–141; and DOROTHY STIMSON, *Scientists and Amateurs: A History of the Royal Society* (New York: Henry Schuman, 1948), pages 169–172. W. JAMES KING, "The Development of Electrical Technology in the 19th Century, Part 1: The Electrochemical Cell and the Electromagnet" (paper 28 in *Contributions from the Museum of History and Technology* [*United States National Museum Bulletin,* 228], Washington: Smithsonian Institution, 1962), pages 234–235.

[7] TIBERIUS CAVALLO, *A Complete Treatise on Electricity in Theory and Practice; With Original Experiments,* fourth edition, 3 volumes (London: C. Dilly, 1795), volume 3, pages 285–286; DIBNER, *Volta,* pages 20, 32, 39, 48, 59 [note 6]; BERN DIBNER, *Galvani-Volta: A Controversy that Led to the Discovery of Useful Chemistry* (Norwalk: Burndy Library, 1952), pages 24–32.

[8] CAVALLO, *Treatise on Electricity,* pages 286–296 [note 7].

[9] JOSEPH HAMEL, "Historical Account of the Introduction of the Galvanic and Electro-Magnetic Telegraph," *The Journal of the Society of Arts, and of the Institutions in Union,* volume 3 (November 1858–November 1859), pages 595–597; W. JAMES KING, "The Development of Electrical Technology in the 19th Century, Part 2: The Telegraph and the Telephone" (paper 29, *Contributions from the Museum of History and Technology* [*United States National Museum Bulletin* 228], Washington: Smithsonian Institution, 1962), pages 276–280, 284–288; A. V. IAROTSKIĬ, *Pavel L'vovich Schilling* (Moscow: Akademii Nauk SSSR, 1963), pages 11–15.

[10] Ibid., pages 14–19; HAMEL, "Introduction of Telegraph," page 598 [note 9].

[11] Ibid. Hamel speaks of Baron Schilling having detonated mines "*across* the river Neva" and "*across* the river Seine," while an account in 1956 by A.V. Khramoi asserts, "After numerous experiments on producing an electric arc (as dis-

covered by V.V. Petrov in 1802) by means of a remote signal, Schilling succeeded in exploding a number of mines set in water on the Neva River." A late nineteenth-century newspaper account cited by Khramoi describes the insulation of Schilling's copper wires with tarred hemp and copper tubing but offers nothing on any waterproofing of the charges themselves. A.V. KHRAMOI, *Ocherk istorii razvitie avtomatiki v SSSR, Dooktyabr'skii period* [History of Automation in Russia before 1917] (Moscow: Izdatel'stvo Akademii Nauk SSSR, 1956), pages 82–84.

12 HAMEL, "Introduction of Telegraph," pages 606–607 [note 9].

13 Ibid., pages 598, 607–609; SAMAROV and PETROV, *Razvitie minnogo*, pages iv–ix, 2–91 [note 2]; ÎAROTSKIĬ, *Schilling*, pages 22–34 [note 9].

14 P. H. KEALY, *General Sir Charles William Pasley, KCB, FRS, DCL, Colonel Commandant R.E., 1780–1861* (London: privately printed, 1930), pages 27–76; H.W. TYLER, "Memoir of General Sir Charles William Pasley, KCB," *Professional Papers of the Corps of Royal Engineers,* new series, volume 12 (1863), pages xii–xiii; *The United States Journal and Naval and Military Magazine* (September 1938), pages 36–48.

15 Ibid. (January 1840), pages 72–83; KEALY, *Pasley,* pages 77–85 [note 14]; *Army and Navy Chronicle and Scientific Repository,* volume 3 (1844), page 744; *The London and Edinburgh Philosophical Magazine and Journal of Science,* volume 10 (January-June 1837), pages 415–417; *Minutes of the Proceedings of the Institution of Civil Engineers,* volume 4 (1833), page 371; *The United Service Journal and Naval and Military Magazine* (January 1840), pages 72–83; L. PEARCE WILLIAMS, editor, *The Selected Correspondence of Michael Faraday,* 2 volumes (Cambridge: Cambridge University Press, 1971), volume 1, pages 329–335.

16 MENDEL L. PETERSON, "Underwater Archaeology," in C.P. IDYLL, editor, *Exploring the Ocean World: A History of Oceanography* (New York: Thomas Y. Crowell Co., 1972), pages 200–202; *Army and Navy Chronicle,* volume 10 (1840), page 100, and volume 11 (1843), pages 417–423; *Journal of the Franklin Institute of the State of Pennsylvania...,* third series, volume 9 (1845), pages 214–215; T.W.J. CONNOLLY, *History of the Royal Sappers and Miners, from the Foundation of the Corps in March 1772 to the Date When its Designation Was Changed to That of Royal Engineers, in October 1856,* 2 volumes (London: Longman, Brown, Green, Longmans and Roberts, 1857), volume 1, pages 348–353.

17 Ibid.; W.B. O'SHAUGHNESSY, "Memorandum of Experiments on the Explosion of Gunpowder under Water by the Galvanic Battery; with a Notice of the Successful Destruction of the Wreck of the 'Equitable,' at Fultah Reach," *Asiatic Society of Bengal Journal,* volume 8 (1839), pages 851–863.

18 BARNES, *Submarine Warfare,* pages 30–52 [note 1]; J. FRANKLIN REIGART, *The Life of Robert Fulton* (Philadelphia: C. G. Henderson, 1856), pages 108–137.

19 EMMANUEL RAYMOND LEWIS, *Seacoast Fortifications of the United States: An Introductory History* (Washington: Smithsonian Institution, 1970), pages 37–42; RUSSELL F. WEIGLEY, *History of the United States Army* (New York: MacMillan Co., 1967), pages 163–164.

20 Samuel Colt to Representative Henry C. Murphy, House Committee on Naval Affairs, 3 June 1844, retained copy, Samuel Colt Papers (manuscripts, Connecticut Historical Society, Hartford), box 6.

21 Compendia of scientific and technical knowledge of the type which Colt studied are compiled in EUGENE S. FERGUSON, *Bibliography of the History of Technology* (Cambridge: Massachusetts Institute of Technology Press, 1968), pages 60–62. For Root's recollections, see HENRY BARNARD's authorized biography, *Armsmear: The Home, the Arm, and the Armory of Samuel Colt: A Memorial* (New York: Alvord, printer, 1866), pages 275–276. See also WILLIAM B. EDWARDS, *The Story of Colt's Revolver: The Biography of Col. Samuel Colt* (Harrisburg: Stackpole Co., 1953), pages 17–19, 159.

22 Ibid., pages 159–160; BARNARD, *Armsmear,* pages 275–276 [note 21]; JACK ROHAN, *Yankee Arms Maker: The Incredible Career of Samuel Colt* (New York: Harper & Brothers, 1935), pages 12–14. See also the manuscript of Colt's lecture on the effects of nitrous oxide, Colt Papers, Misc. MSS 73561.

23 EDWARD FAHS SMITH, *The Life of Robert Hare: An American Chemist, 1781–1858* (Philadelphia: J.B. Lippincott Co., 1917), pages 3–12, 62–67, 325, 371–384; ROBERT HARE, "Account of New Eudiometers, &c.," *The American Journal of Science and Arts,* volume 2 (1820), pages 312–318, and plates at end of volume.

24 ROBERT HARE, "Description of a Process and an Apparatus for Blasting Rocks by Means of Galvanic Ignition," *Journal of the Franklin Institute,* volume 12 (1833), pages 221–226; HENRY L. ABBOT, "Report upon Experiments and Investigations to Develop a System of Submarine Mines for Defending the Harbors of the United States" (number 23 in *Professional Papers of the Corps of Engineers, U.S. Army,* Washington, Government Printing Office, 1881), page 252.

25 HARE, "Apparatus for Blasting Rocks," pages 221–222 [note 24].

26 Ibid., page 223; *Letter from the Secretary of War Relative to the Secret of Colt's Submarine Battery, May 15, 1844, Referred to the Committee on Naval Affairs, February 8, 1845,* 28th Congress, 2nd Session, House Document Number 127, pages 12–13.

27 HARE, "Apparatus for Blasting Rocks," page 226 [note 24].

28 Colonel Joseph G. Totten to Major General Joseph G. Swift, 15 May 1832, in Letters and Reports of Col. Joseph G. Totten, 1803–1864, 10 volumes, National Archives, Record Group 77, Entry 146, volume 2, pages 358–360. In addition to Totten's official and private correspondence in Entry 146, see also Entry 223, Reports of Boards of Engineers Relating to Fortifications and Defenses; and Entry 457, Letters Received by Board of Engineers for Fortifications [Bernard Board], 1825–1830.

29 See Colonel George Bomford, U.S. Ordnance Office to Colt, 2 March 1841, Colt Papers, box 2: EDWARDS, *Colt's Revolver,* pages 21–155, 160, 178–179, 191–207 [note 21]; SAMUEL IRENAEUS PRIME, *The Life of Samuel F.B. Morse, LL.D, Inventor of the Electro-Magnetic Recording Tele-*

graph (New York: D. Appleton & Co., 1875), pages 436–439; BERKELEY R. LEWIS, "Small Arms and Ammunition in the United States Service, 1776–1865" (number 129 in *Smithsonian Miscellaneous Collections,* Washington: Smithsonian Institution, 1960), pages 53–55, 122–124.

30 Colt to Representative Murphy, 3 June 1844, Colt Papers, box 6; SAMUEL FLAGG BEMIS, *A Diplomatic History of the United States,* 4th edition (New York: Henry Holt & Co., 1955), pages 287–291. The Paterson sketch and subsequently cited drawings are, unless otherwise noted, found in the Samuel Colt Collection, located at the Connecticut State Library Museum in Hartford. Colt's patent petition of 8 June 1844 for the Submarine Battery, which complements these drawings, is found in the Colt Papers, box 6, at the Connecticut Historical Society, Hartford.

31 See drawing "E" in Colt Collection.

32 See drawings "A" and "F" in Colt Collection.

33 Colt to Captain A. Partridge, 5 August 1841, retained copy, and A. Partridge to Colt, 9 August 1841, Colt Papers, box 6. See also the manuscript diary of Samuel Colt, 1836–1837, Colt Papers, box 1; Colt's subscription receipt for B. Homan's *Army and Navy Chronicle* for 1840; and articles on Colonel Pasley's operations in the *Army and Navy Chronicle,* volume 8 (1839), pages 373–375; volume 9 (1839), pages 222, 270, 287, 294, 356–357, 389; and volume 10 (1840), page 100.

34 A typical referral from the Board of Navy Commissioners to the Ordnance Office of the War Department is cited in Commodore Isaac Chauncy to Colt, 24 July 1835, Colt Papers, box 9. See box 10 for Colt's outraged "Preparation for trying tin foil cartridges," dated 31 March–3 April 1840, recounting his experience at the Washington Arsenal; EDWARDS, *Colt's Revolver,* pages 144–148, 159–161 [note 21].

35 Ibid.; Colt to President John Tyler, 19 June 1841, retained copy, Colt Papers, box 5; Senator Southard to President Tyler, 21 June 1841, courtesy copy, Colt Papers, box 5; Colt to Representative Murphy, 3 June 1844, retained copy, Colt Papers, box 6.

36 WALTER LOWRIE and WALTER S. FRANKLIN, editors, *American State Papers: Documents, Legislative and Executive, of the Congress of the United States,* 38 volumes (Washington: Gales and Seaton, 1832–1861), *Naval Affairs,* volume 1, pages 211–227.

37 Colt to President Tyler, 19 June 1841, retained copy, Colt Papers, box 5.

38 Ibid.

39 Ibid.; Colt to Secretary of the Navy George E. Badger, 2 July 1841, retained copy, Colt Papers, box 5; Secretary Badger to Senator Southard, 20 July 1841, courtesy copy, Colt Papers, box 5; ROBERT SEAGER II, *And Tyler Too: A Biography of John and Julia Gardiner Tyler* (New York: McGraw-Hill Book Co., 1963), pages 151–157; EDWARDS, *Colt's Revolver,* pages 161–163 [note 21].

40 The identity of Colt's Russian visitors doubtless lies in the Soviet naval archives. Captain von Schantz may well have been accompanied by two members of his mission, Captain Pypin' and Lieutenant Sharubin', both of the Engineer Corps, who were reported by the *Army and Navy Chronile* (volume 9, page 124) on 8 August 1842 to be concluding a year's tour of the United States maritime establishment, having given particular attention to steam navigation. The Russian naval mission had been active in the United States since 1837. Captain von Schantz took command of the steam frigate *Kamchatka* upon her departure from New York for Kronstadt in September 1841. See EDWARDS, *Colt's Revolver,* pages 128, 140, 161–162 [note 21]; *Niles' National Register,* volume 61 (2 October 1841), page 80; S.O. OGORODNIKOV, *Istoricheskii obzor razvitiia i deiatel'nosti morskogo ministerstva za sto let evo sushchestvovania* [Historical Review of the Development and Activities of the Ministry of Marine in the Hundred Years of its Existence] (St. Petersburg: Tipografia morskogo ministerstva, 1902), page 127.

41 Colt to Senator Samuel Southard, 8 July 1841, retained copy, Colt Papers, box 5. Regarding Warner's Destroyer, see *Army and Navy Chronicle,* volume 9 (1839), page 158; and *Army and Navy Chronicle and Scientific Repository,* volume 2 (1843), pages 449–452.

42 SAMAROV and PETROV, editors, *Razvitie minnogo,* pages 2–91 [note 2].

43 Colt visited St. Petersburg in 1856, following up substantial Russian orders for his arms after the Crimean War. EDWARDS, *Colt's Revolver,* pages 320–321 [note 21]. Regarding the career of Immanuel Nobel in Russia, see ERIK BERGENGREN, *Alfred Nobel: The Man and His Work* (London: Thomas Nelson, 1962), pages 7–15.

44 EDWARDS, *Colt's Revolver,* pages 163–164 [note 21]; SEAGER, *Tyler,* pages 158–162 [note 39].

45 Colt to C.B.D. Ogden, 9 October 1841, retained copy, Colt Papers, box 5; SEAGER, *Tyler,* pages 164–165, 205 [note 39]; EDWARDS, *Colt's Revolver,* pages 164, 170–171 [note 21].

46 Colt to Representative Murphy, 3 June 1844; and Colt to Secretary of the Navy Abel P. Upshur, 12 November 1841, retained copy, Colt Papers, box 5.

47 Colt to Secretary Upshur, 24 November 1841, retained copy, Colt Papers, box 5. Regarding the absence of reference to Colt's Submarine Battery in the deliberations of the Board of Navy Commissioners, see the following entries at the National Archives in Record Group 45: Entry 209—Journal (Rough Minutes) of the Board of Navy Commissioners, volume 20 (22 February–23 September 1842); Entry 219—Navy Commissioners' Office Journal, volume 13 (1 September 1840–5 April 1842); Entry 219—Board of Navy Commissioners' Office, Miscellaneous Letters 1 January–25 August 1842).

48 Colt to Senator Southard, 2 January 1842, retained copy, Colt Papers, box 6.

49 Secretary Upshur to Colt, 25 November 1841, Colt Papers, box 5.

50 See the legal instrument for incorporation of the Submarine Battery Company, notarized by Colt on 18 December 1841, with appended list of subscribers, in Colt Papers, box 5.

51 Colt to Senator Southard, 2 January 1842, retained copy, Colt Papers, box 6; FRANK M. BENNETT, *The Steam Navy of the United States: A History of the Growth of the Steam Vessel of War in the U.S. Navy, and of the Naval Engineer Corps* (Pittsburgh: Warren & Co., 1896), page 75.

52 See Brown and Elton to Colt, 6 January and 4 May

1842; and Colt to Brown and Elton, 13 January 1842, retained copy, Colt Papers, box 6.

[53] Colt to Professor John William Draper, 10 March 1842, retained copy, Colt Papers, box 6; PRIME, *Morse*, pages 436–438 [note 29]; EDWARDS, *Colt's Revolver*, pages 160, 191–193 [note 21]. See also Appendix 6, paragraph 6.

[54] Colt to Secretary Upshur, 12 March 1842, retained copy, Colt Papers, box 6.

[55] PRIME, *Morse*, pages 437–438 [note 29].

[56] Colt's sketches of Silas Clowden Halsey's submersible and torpedo were based on information he secured from Captain Jeremiah Holmes of Mystic and others and are found in Colt Papers, box 6. See also in that respository Luther Sargent to Colt, 21 February 1842.

[57] U.S. Congress, *The Debates and Proceedings in the Congress of the United States. . . , Twelfth Congress, Second Session* (Washington: Gales and Seaton, 1853), pages 83–95, 102–106, 1168, 1346; [Hezekiah Niles] *The Weekly Register*, volume 4 (1813), pages 293, 308–309, 325–327, 337, 340, 344, 365–367, 375.

[58] Colt to Senator Southard, 23 February 1842, retained copy, Colt Papers, box 6.

[59] Colt to Senator Southard, 28 February 1842, retained copy Colt Papers, box 6; BENNETT, *Steam Navy*, pages 57–60 [note 51].

[60] Ibid.; Colt to Brown and Elton, 2 June 1842, Colt Papers, box 6; EDWARDS, *Colt's Revolver*, page 174 [note 21].

[61] *The Scientific American*, volume 1, number 12 (4 December 1845), page 46; GEORGE B. PRESCOTT, *Electricity and the Electric Telegraph*, 4th edition (New York: D. Appleton & Co., 1881), pages 64–66.

[62] Colt to Secretary Upshur, 7 May 1842, retained copy, Colt Papers, box 6; Cole's Diary, 4 June 1842, Colt Papers, box 16–17.

[63] Colt to Edward Curtice, 25 April 1841 and 24 May 1842, retained copies, Colt Papers, boxes 2 and 6, respectively; *Army and Navy Chronicle*, volume 11 (1840), page 183.

[64] New York *Evening Post*, 5 July 1842; *Alexandria Gazette and Virginia Advertiser*, 8 July 1842; Washington *Daily National Intelligencer*, 8 July 1842.

[65] New York *American*, quoted in *Niles' National Register*, volume 62 (16 July 1842), page 310.

[66] Colt to Secretary Upshur, 5 July 1842, in Miscellaneous Letters Received by the Secretary of the Navy, 1 July–31 August 1842, National Archives, Record Group 45, Entry 21, Microcopy 124, Roll 185.

[67] New York *Herald*, 6 July 1842.

[68] New York *Sun*, quoted in *Niles' National Register*, volume 62 (16 July 1842), page 310; see also aforementioned Miscellaneous Letters Received by the Secretary of the Navy, 1 July–21 August 1842; and Navy Commissioners' Office, Letters Received from New York Navy Yard, 5 May–13 July 1842, National Archives, Record Group 45, Entry 220.

[69] Secretary Upshur to Colt, 5 and 11 July 1842, Colt Papers, box 6.

[70] Colt to Secretary Upshur, 5 July 1842, retained copy, Colt Papers, box 6.

[71] The Board of Navy Commissioners had received correspondence from Samuel Colt relating to his firearms on 3 March 1842, but there is no evidence that his Submarine Battery came to its official attention, aside from a request, evidently prompted by Upshur, that it submitted to Lt. Col. George Talcott of the Ordnance Office of the War Department for fifteen barrels of powder for Colt's Washington demonstration of 20 August 1842. See Board of Navy Commissioners to Colonel Talcott, 15 August 1842, retained copy, Navy Commissioners' Office, Miscellaneous Letters, volume 8 (2 September 1839–31 August 1842), National Archives, Record Group 45, Entry 217; Board of Navy Commissioners Miscellaneous In-Letters, 1 July–25 August 1842, National Archives, Record Group 45, Entry 219; and Journal (Rough Minutes) of the Board of Navy Commissioners, volume 20 (22 February–23 September 1842), National Archives, Record Group 45, Entry 209.

[72] Secretary Upshur to Colt, 11 July 1842, Colt Papers, box 6; CHARLES OSCAR PAULLIN, *Paullin's History of Naval Administration, 1775–1911: A Collection of Articles from the U.S. Naval Institute Proceedings* (Annapolis: United States Naval Institute, 1968), pages 208–211; STEPHEN V. BENET, editor, *A Collection of Annual Reports and Other Important Papers Relating to the Ordnance Department. . . ,* 4 volumes (Washington: Government Printing Office, 1878–1890), volume 1, pages 342–344, 356–357, 364–366; *Army and Navy Chronicle*, volume 13 (1842), pages 267–269.

[73] *Congressional Globe*, volume 11, number 44 (2 July 1842), pages 689–690.

[74] Ibid., volume 11, number 59 (25 August 1842), page 939; EDWARDS, *Colt's Revolver*, page 175 [note 21]; Colt to Representative John Quincy Adams, 11 August 1842, retained copy, Colt Papers, box 6, with annotation, "To the above letter no answer was received." See also Colt Diary, 2 August 1842, Colt Papers, box 16–17.

[75] CHARLES FRANCIS ADAMS, editor, *Memoirs of John Quincy Adams, Comprising Portions of His Diary from 1795 to 1848,* 12 volumes (Philadelphia: J.B. Lippincott & Co., 1874–1877), volume 11, page 219.

[76] Board of Navy Commissioners to Lt. Col. George Talcott, 15 August 1842; Secretary Upshur to Colt, 18 August 1842, retained copy, in Miscellaneous Letters Sent by the Secretary of the Navy, 1798–1886, volume 33, National Archives, Record Group 45, Entry 3; Colt to Secretary of the Navy John Y. Mason, 22 April 1844, retained copy, Colt Papers, box 6; Captain Beverly Kennon to Secretary Upshur, 17 August 1842, in Captains' Letters Received by the Secretary of the Navy, 1–31 August 1842, National Archives, Record Group 45, Microcopy 125, Roll 292; Captain Kennon to Colt, 27 August 1842, Colt Papers, box 6; Journal of the Navy Yard at Washington, 11 August–2 September 1842, National Archives, Record Group 71, Entry 91.

[77] Colt to Chief Clerk John D. Simms, 6 September 1842, retained copy, Colt Papers, box 6.

[78] EDWARDS, *Colt's Revolver*, page 175 [note 21]; *Alexandria Gazette and Virginia Advertiser*, 20 August 1842; Washington *Daily National Intelligencer*, 19 and 22 August 1842.

[79] Ibid.; Board of Navy Commissioners to Colonel Talcott, 15 August 1842, National Archives, Record Group 45, Entry

3; Captain Kennon to Colt, 27 August 1842, Colt Papers, box 6.

[80] Anonymous, "United States Patent Office," in *The United States Magazine,* volume 3 (1856), page 470; *Bulletin of the Proceedings of the National Institution for the Promotion of Science,* volume 1 (1841).

[81] Ibid., volume 1 (1841), pages 1–2; SALLY KOHLSTEDT, "A Step toward Scientific Self-Identity in the United States: The Failure of the National Institute, 1844," *Isis,* volume 62 (1971), pages 339-346; GEORGE B. GOODE, editor, *The Smithsonian Institution, 1846–1896* (Washington: Smithsonian Institution, 1897), pages 25–31, 37–42; WILLIAM J. RHEES, editor, *The Smithsonian Institution: Documents Relative to its Origin and History* (number 328 in *Smithsonian Miscellaneous Collections,* Washington: Smithsonian Institution, 1879), pages 1–2, 146–148.

[82] DAVID B. TYLER, *The Wilkes Expedition: The First United States Exploring Expedition, 1838-1842* (Philadelphia: American Philosophical Society, 1968), pages 387–391; *Proceedings of the National Institution,* volume 1, pages 75–79, 119–120; and volume 3, pages 239–243, 249, 259.

[83] Ibid., volume 3, page 250. See War Department Circular of 9 July 1842 published in Washington *Daily National Intelligencer,* 21 October 1842; *Army and Navy Chronicle,* volume 13 (1842), page 471.

[84] Ibid., volume 13 (1842), pages 619–623; Francis Markoe, Corresponding Secretary of the National Institution, to Colt, 22 August 1840, Colt Papers, box 2; *Proceedings of the National Institution,* volume 1 (1841), pages 1–2, 17–18, 139–142.

[85] New York *Evening Post,* 24 August 1842.

[86] Ibid.; *Niles' National Register,* volume 62 (27 August 1842), page 416.

[87] Washington *Daily National Intelligencer,* 22 August 1842.

[88] Ibid. See also drawing "G" or "No. 5" in Colt Collection, Connecticut State Library Museum, Hartford.

[89] Colt to Secretary Mason, 22 April 1844, retained copy, Colt Papers, box 6. BARNARD, *Armsmear,* pages 280–281 [note 21].

[90] Ibid.; New York *Evening Post,* 23 August 1842; Washington *Daily National Intelligencer,* 22 August 1842.

[91] Colt to Representative Murphy, 3 June 1844, retained copy. Colt Papers, box 6.

[92] Ibid.; Colt to Representative Edward Stanly, 21 August 1842, retained copy, Colt Papers, box 6; *Congressional Globe,* volume 11 (1842), page 930.

[93] Ibid.; *Army and Navy Chronicle,* volume 9 (1839), pages 371–372.

[94] *Congressional Globe,* volume 11 (1842), page 930; BARNARD, *Armsmear,* pages 282–284 [note 21].

[95] Ibid.; *Niles' National Register,* volume 62 (1842), page 415; See also Colt's annotated record of the House vote in Colt Papers, box 6.

[96] *Congressional Globe,* volume 11 (1842) pages 949–950, 962, 977; CHARLES M. WILTSE, *John C. Calhoun, Nationalist, 1782-1828* (New York: Bobbs-Merrill, 1944), pages 107–248.

[97] Secretary Upshur to Lieutenant Matthew Fontaine Maury, 31 August 1842, and Colt to Secretary Upshur, 31 August 1842, retained copy, Colt Papers, box 6. Regarding Maury, see FRANCES LEIGH WILLIAMS, *Matthew Fontaine Maury, Scientist of the Sea* (New Brunswick, N.J.: Rutgers University Press, 1963), pages 144–150; the Matthew Fontaine Maury Papers (Manuscript Division, Library of Congress); and the Maury Family Papers (Manuscripts Department, Alderson Library, University of Virginia at Charlottesville).

[98] Colt appears to have spent much of 31 August in a vain effort to see Secretary Upshur before departing for New York. See drawing "U," a rough chart of the Potomac and Eastern Branch, evidently used for the final Washington experiments in 1844, Colt Collection, Connecticut State Library Museum, Hartford.

[99] WILLIAMS, *Maury,* pages 144–268 [note 97]. By 1843, Maury's journalistic efforts were turning to the advocacy of naval construction on the Western rivers. For his earlier "Scraps from the Lucky Bag," published under the pseudonym "Harry Bluff," see *The Southern Literary Messenger,* volume 5 (1839), pages 233–240; volume 6 (1840), pages 306–320, 785–800; and volume 7 (1841), pages 3–25, 345–378, 560–563.

[100] WILLIAMS, *Maury,* pages 367–370, 376–394 [note 97]; MILTON F. PERRY, *Infernal Machines: The Story of Confederate Submarine and Mine Warfare* (Baton Rouge: Louisiana State University Press, 1965), pages 4–19.

[101] See the Maury Papers, Library of Congress, and the Maury Family Papers, Alderman Library [note 97].

[102] *Alexandria Gazette and Virginia Advertiser,* 5 October 1842.

[103] Drawing "G" ("No. 5"), Colt Collection, Connecticut State Library Museum, Hartford.

[104] Drawing "I," Colt Collection.

[105] *Alexandria Gazette and Virginia Advertiser,* 5 October 1842.

[106] Ibid.

[107] George C. De Kay to President John Tyler, 5 August 1842; and De Kay to Secretary Upshur, 6 September 1842, both courtesy copies, Colt Papers, box 6.

[108] Colt to Chief Clerk John D. Simms, 12 September 1842, retained copy, Colt Papers, box 6.

[109] Secretary Upshur to De Kay, 12 September 1842, courtesy copy, Colt Papers, box 6.

[110] Secretary Upshur to Colt, 27 September 1842, Colt Papers, box 6.

[111] Colt to Major William G. McNeill, 27 September 1842, retained copy, Colt Papers, box 6; New York *Herald,* 27 and 28 September 1842; ROHAN, *Yankee Arms Maker,* pages 140–141 [note 22]; EDWARDS, *Colt's Revolver,* page 177 [note 21].

[112] Ibid.; Colt to Secretary Upshur, 30 September and 6 October 1842, retained copies; and Secretary Upshur to Colt, 18 October 1842, all in Colt Papers, box 6.

[113] Secretary Upshur to Colt, 7 October 1842; and De Kay to Colt, 12 October 1842, Colt Papers, box 6.

[114] Samuel F.B. Morse to Colt, 22 October 1842, Colt Papers, box 6; New York *Herald,* 19 October 1842; CARLETON MABEE, *The American Leonardo: A Life of Samuel*

F.B. Morse (New York: Alfred A. Knopf, 1942), pages 250–251; EDWARDS, *Colt's Revolver,* pages 178–179 [note 21].

[115] See Colt's invitation of Brigadier General William J. Worth, USA, 18 October 1842, retained copy, Colt Papers, box 6; New York *Evening Post,* 19 October 1842; *Niles' National Register,* volume 13 (1842), page 128; New York *Express,* quoted in *Alexandria Gazette and Virginia Advertiser,* 20 October 1842.

[116] Colt to Secretary Upshur, 19 October 1842, retained copy, Colt Papers, box 6.

[117] Ibid.

[118] *Niles' National Register,* volume 13 (1842), page 128.

[119] Washington *Daily National Intelligencer,* 21 October 1842. See also New York *Evening Post,* 19 October 1842, and New York *Herald,* 19 October 1842.

[120] See entry on 18 October 1842 in "Monthly Extracts taken from the Journal of the U.S. Rev. Cutter *Ewing,* Alexdr B. Fraser, Esq., Commd., Beginning 1st Ending 31st Oct. 1842," in Treasury Department, Logbooks of Revenue Cutters, 1842–1843, National Archives, Record Group 26; Colt to Secretary of the Navy John Y. Mason, 22 April 1844, retained copy, Colt Papers, box 6; BARNARD, *Armsmear,* page 284 [note 21].

[121] Colt's conception of a two-observer minefield at this juncture is sketched in Colt to Secretary Upshur, 6 October 1842, retained copy, marked "private," Colt Papers, box 6.

[122] New York *Herald,* 19 October 1842.

[123] Colt to Secretary Upshur, 19 October 1842, retained copy, Colt Papers, box 6.

[124] *Congressional Globe,* volume 11 (1842), page 930.

[125] New York *Herald,* 19 October 1842; EDWARDS, *Colt's Revolver,* pages 178–179 [note 21]; EDWARD LIND MORSE, editor, *Samuel F. B. Morse: His Letters and Journals,* 2 volumes (Boston: Houghton Mifflin Co., 1914), volume 2, pages 182–184.

[126] Ibid.; Morse to Colt, 28 November 1842, and second undated letter believed to be of the same period, sent from Morse to Colt, Colt Papers, box 6.

[127] MORSE, *Morse,* volume 2, pages 185–186 [note 125]; PRESCOTT, *Electric Telegraph,* pages 768–867 [note 61]; Morse to Colt, 22 October 1842, Colt Papers, box 6; KING, "Development of Electrical Technology, Part 2," pages 295–300 [note 9].

[128] Colt to Samuel Whiting, 17 June 1845, retained copy, Colt Papers, box 5–7; EDWARDS, *Colt's Revolver,* pages 192–203, and appendix [note 21]; MORSE, *Morse,* volume 2, pages 184–203 [note 125].

[129] Regarding the final melodrama surrounding the apparent death of John Colt and the disappearance of his widow, see the New York *Herald,* 20 November 1842; EDWARDS, *Colt's Revolver,* pages 179–184 [note 21]; and FREDERICK W. SEWARD, editor, *Autobiography of William H. Seward, from 1801 to 1834 . . .* (New York: D. Appleton & Co., 1877); pages 630–635.

[130] Colt to Brown and Elton, 13 and 16 January 1843, retained copies, Brown and Elton to Colt, 31 January and 7 February 1843, all in Colt Papers, box 6.

[131] See records of Colt's experiments 7 February, 23 March, 15 and 25 April 1843, Colt Papers, box 6; and Colt's account book, January–May 1843, Colt Papers, box 16–17.

[132] Record of Colt's experiment at "New York University," 23 March 1843, Colt Papers, box 6.

[133] *Army and Navy Chronicle and Scientific Repository,* volume 1 (1843), page 570.

[134] Colt to David Henshaw, 30 August 1843, retained copy, and bill of sale for the barque *Brunette,* dated 30 October 1843, Colt Papers, box 6; EDWARDS, *Colt's Revolver,* pages 149–150.

[135] Records of Colt's experiments of 3 and 15 August, 1 September 1843, and of 3 February 1844, Colt Papers, box 6.

[136] *Army and Navy Chronicle and Scientific Repository,* volume 2 (1843), pages 413–414, 694–695, 762; BENNETT, *Steam Navy,* pages 57–60 [note 51].

[137] Stephen Shinn to Colt, 29 November and 16 December 1843; and Colt to Shinn, 6 December 1843, retained copy, all in Colt Papers, box 6.

[138] *Alexandria Gazette and Virginia Advertiser,* 29 February, 1 and 2 March 1844; *Army and Navy Chronicle and Scientific Repository,* volume 3 (1844), pages 281–282; HARRY C. WATTS, "Ericsson, Stockton and the U.S.S. *Princeton,*" *United States Naval Institute Proceedings,* volume 82 (1956), pages 964–967.

[139] *Alexandria Gazette and Virginia Advertiser,* 22 March 1844; *Army and Navy Chronicle and Scientific Repository,* volume 3 (1844), pages 341–342; chart of Potomac River and Eastern Branch, Colt Collection, Connecticut State Library Museum, Hartford. See Colt to Acting Secretary of the Navy Lewis Warrington, 11 March 1844, retained copy; Commodore Warrington to Captain John H. Aulick, Commandant, Washington Navy Yard, 13 March 1844, courtesy copy; Colt to Captain Aulick, 15 March 1844, retained copy, all in Colt Papers, box 6; *Congressional Globe,* volume 14 (1844), pages 415, 419.

[140] Colt to Representative Henry A. Wise, 1 April 1844, retained copy, Colt Papers, box 6.

[141] Washington *Daily National Intelligencer,* 12 April 1844; Washington *Madisonian,* 9 and 15 April 1844; *Alexandria Gazette and Virginia Advertiser,* 15 April 1844.

[142] On 9 April Morse successfully demonstrated his electromagnetic telegraph line between Bladensburg and Washington. Ibid., 28 March and 3 April 1844; Washington *Madisonian,* 10 April 1844; *Army and Navy Chronicle and Scientific Repository,* volume 2 (1843), pages 141–145, and volume 3 (1844), pages 625–630; *Proceedings of the National Institute,* volume 3 (1844), page 437ff.

[143] SAMUEL FLAGG BEMIS, editor, *The American Secretaries of State and their Diplomacy,* 18 volumes (New York: Alfred A. Knopf, Inc., Pageant Book Co., and Cooper Square Publishers, 1958–1970), volume 5, pages 88–121, 136–171. KOHLSTEDT, "Failure of the National Institute," pages 339–340, 356–360 [note 81].

[144] *Alexandria Gazette and Virginia Advertiser,* 13 March 1844; Baltimore *American,* 11 March 1844; THEODORE F. RODENBOUGH and WILLIAM L. HASKIN, editors, *The Army of the United States: Historical Sketches of Staff and Line, with Portraits of Generals-in-Chief* (New York: Military Service Institution, 1896), pages 332, 335–336; *Congressional Globe,* volume 13 (1844), page 374.

[145] Ibid.

[146] Ibid., volume 13 (1844), pages 533–535; *Alexandria Gazette and Virginia Advertiser,* 15 April 1844.

[147] Ibid.

[148] See in particular the extended accounts of one "Sigma" in the Washington *Daily National Intelligencer,* 15 April 1844, and of "Peter Primrose" in the Washington *Madisonian,* 17 April 1844, efforts that merit stylistic comparison.

[149] Ibid. The unsigned sketch of Colt's demonstration off the Washington Navy Yard, designated drawing "B," is found in the Colt Collection at the Connecticut State Library Museum, Hartford.

[150] Ibid. Lieutenant Boyle's schedule of signals for the destruction of the *Styx* are contained in an undated document, "Signals Ship Styx," in the Colt Papers, box 6.

[151] Washington *Daily National Intelligencer,* 15 April 1844.

[152] Washington *Madisonian,* 17 April 1844.

[153] Washington *Daily National Intelligencer,* 15 April 1844. Colt's statement regarding his position during this demonstration is contained in his letter to Secretary of the Navy John Y. Mason, 22 April 1844, retained copy, Colt Papers, box 6. The "study for a pencil" suggested by "Sigma" may indeed be the aforementioned drawing "B."

[154] See unsigned article, "The Sub-Marine Battery," Washington *Daily National Intelligencer,* 15 April 1844.

[155] Colt to Secretary Mason, 22 April 1844, retained copy, Colt Papers, box 6.

[156] Ibid. In an early draft of this report, also in the Colt Papers, box 6, the inventor increased his original estimate from "My battery was a mile distant from the ship . . . ," to "something more than 2 miles. . . ."

[157] Ibid.; Colt to Representative Henry C. Murphy, 3 June 1844, retained copy, Colt Papers, box 6; drawing "U" in Colt Collection, Connecticut State Library Museum, Hartford.

[158] Compare drawing "B" in Colt Collection and the oil painting by Aⁿ. Gibert in the collection of Mr. Caldwell C. Robinson, Trappe, Maryland. Colt's receipt for payment to Gibert on 15 October 1844 of $60.00 for this painting is found in Colt Papers, box 16–17. See also ALLEN C. CLARK, *Greenleaf and Law in the Federal City* (Washington: W.F. Roberts Press, 1901), page 246.

[159] Washington *Daily National Intelligencer,* 15 April 1844.

[160] *Army and Navy Chronicle and Scientific Repository,* volume 3 (1844), page 509.

[161] Washington *Daily National Intelligencer,* 19, 20, and 22 April 1844; *Alexandria Gazette and Virginia Advertiser,* 22 April 1844.

[162] TAYLOR PECK, *Round Shot to Rockets: A History of the Washington Navy Yard and Gun Factory* (Annapolis: United States Naval Institute, 1949), pages 102–103.

[163] Washington *Daily National Intelligencer,* 15–23 April 1844; SEAGER, *Tyler,* pages 209–230 [note 39]; BEMIS, *American Secretaries of State,* volume 5, pages 136–171 [note 143].

[164] *Congressional Globe,* volume 13 (1844), page 562; Colt memorial to the Senate and House of Representatives, 16 April 1844, retained copy, Colt Papers, box 6.

[165] *Congressional Globe,* volume 13 (1844), page 562.

[166] Colt to Major William Gibbs McNeill, 22 April 1844, retained copy, Colt Papers, box 6.

[167] Ibid.; Colt to Secretary Mason, 22 April 1844, retained copy, Colt Papers, box 6.

[168] Ibid.; Secretary Mason to Secretary of War William Wilkins, 7 May 1844, in *Colt's Submarine Battery,* House Document No. 127, 28th Congress, 2nd Session, page 5.

[169] Colt to Secretary Mason, 25 April 1844, in Miscellaneous Letters Received by the Secretary of the Navy, 1801–1884, National Archives, Record Group 45, Microcopy 124, Roll 204; Colt to Secretary Mason, 24 April 1844, retained copy, Colt Papers, box 6; Secretary Mason to Colt, 26 April 1844, Colt Papers, box 6.

[170] Colt to Secretary Mason, 1 May 1844, retained copy, Colt Papers, box 6.

[171] Ibid.; Secretary of War William Wilkins to the Honorable J.W. Jones, Speaker of the House of Representatives, 8 May 1844, in *Colt's Submarine Battery,* page 1 [note 168].

[172] Colt to Secretary Wilkins, 22 April 1844, retained copy, Colt Papers, box 6.

[173] Secretary Wilkins to Colt, 27 April 1844, Colt Papers, box 6.

[174] Colt to Secretary Wilkins, 30 April 1844, retained copy, Colt Papers, box 6.

[175] Secretary Mason to Secretary Wilkins, 7 May 1844, in *Colt's Submarine Battery,* page 5 [note 168].

[176] Colt to Secretary Wilkins, 8 May 1844, in ibid., pages 5–6.

[177] Professor Robert Hare to Secretary Wilkins, 1 May 1844, in ibid., pages 12–14.

[178] Ibid. See drawing "F" in Colt Collection, Connecticut State Library Museum, Hartford.

[179] Samuel F. B. Morse to Joseph Henry, 30 April 1844, in Joseph Henry Papers, Smithsonian Institution Archives: NATHAN REINGOLD, editor, *Science in Nineteenth Century America: A Documentary History* (New York: Hill and Wang Co., 1964) pages 62–65, 152–155; THOMAS COULSON, *Joseph Henry: His Life and His Work* (Princeton: Princeton University Press, 1950), pages 46–186; MORSE, *Morse,* pages 170–173 [note 125]; PRIME, *Morse,* pages 419–423, 437–438 [note 29].

[180] Compare Professor Henry's description of a platinum fuse mine with that provided by Colt in the *Alexandria Gazette and Virginia Advertiser,* 5 October 1842 [p. 32, herein].

[181] Joseph Henry to Secretary Wilkins, 3 May 1844, in *Colt's Submarine Battery,* pages 16–17 [note 168]. See also Henry's retained copy, with minor variations, in the Joseph Henry Papers, Smithsonian Institution Archives, Washington, D.C.

[182] *Army and Navy Chronicle and Scientific Repository,* volume 1 (1843), page 570; Samuel F. B. Morse to Joseph Henry, 30 April 1844, in Joseph Henry Papers, Smithsonian Institution Archives, Washington, D.C.; REINGOLD, *Science in Nineteenth Century America,* pages 63–65 [note 179].

[183] Henry to Secretary Wilkins, 3 May 1844, in *Colt's Submarine Battery,* pages 16–17 [note 168].

[184] GEORGE W. CULLUM, *Biographical Register of the Officers and Graduates of the United States Military Academy,* 3rd edition, 2 volumes (Boston: Houghton, Mifflin Co., 1891), volume 1, pages 63–67.

185 Colonel Joseph G. Totten to Secretary Wilkins, 1 May 1844, in *Colt's Submarine Battery*, pages 6–11 [note 168].

186 Ibid.

187 Ibid.

188 Ibid.

189 Ibid.

190 Secretary Wilkins to House Speaker J.W. Jones, 8 May 1844, in ibid., pages 1–3; *Army and Navy Chronicle and Scientific Repository*, volume 3 (1844), page 744.

191 *Colt's Submarine Battery*, page 1 [note 168].

192 Colt to Representative Murphy, 3 June 1844, in Colt Papers, box 6.

193 House Committee on Naval Affairs, Report No. 46, on Samuel Colt, 11 January 1845, in *Colt's Submarine Battery*, House Document No. 127, 28th Congress, 2nd Session, page 20 [note 168]; Representative Murphy to Henry L. Ellsworth, 4 June 1844, courtesy copy in Colt Papers, box 6.

194 Patent Petition of Samuel Colt of New York, New York, 8 June 1844, Colt Papers, box 6. The annotations to Colt's patent drawing number 3 are believed to have been added subsequent to 1860 by Charles B. Richards ("c.b.r."), who served as engineering superintendent of the Colt Armory in Hartford during Colt's last years. JOSEPH WICKHAM ROE, *English and American Tool Builders* (New Haven: Yale University Press, 1971), page 172.

195 House Committee on Naval Affairs, Report No. 46, in *Colt's Submarine Battery*, pages 20–21 [note 168].

196 Thomas P. Jones to Colt, 14 June 1844, in ibid., page 24 (see also page 21).

197 House Committee on Naval Affairs, Report No. 46, in ibid., page 20.

198 As ultimately stated by the House Committee on Naval Affairs, this objection had lost Colonel Totten's very valid warning about the ineffectiveness of an observation system in darkness or lowered visibility. Ibid., pages 2, 10, and 21.

199 Ibid., page 22.

200 Commissioner Henry L. Ellsworth to Colt, 8 June 1844, Colt Papers, box 6; BARNARD, *Armsmear*, page 297 [note 21].

201 *Congressional Globe*, volume 4 (1845), page 126. See also "A Bill for the Relief of Samuel Colt...," House Resolution No. 519, 29th Congress, 2nd Session, in Colt Papers, box 6.

202 Secretary Mason to Representative John Stewart of the House Committee on Naval Affairs, 13 February 1845, courtesy copy, Colt Papers, box 6.

203 Ibid.

204 Report of Col. Joseph G. Totten, Col. John J. Abert and Lt. Col. George Talcott to Secretary of War William Wilkins regarding inventions of George W. Taylor of Boston, 4 February 1845, in Letters and Reports of Col. Joseph G. Totten, Chief of Engineers, Record Group 77, Entry 147, volume 6, pages 76–83; Col. Totten to Senator Thomas Hart Benton, 28 December 1844, in ibid., volume 6, pages 68–69. See also Colt to President Tyler, 19 June 1841, Colt Papers, box 5.

205 A major portion of Colt's equipment, including four batteries, anchor chain, twenty-five iron canisters, fifteen pounds of powder and sixteen spools, shipped to New York in the schooner *Alexandria*, was attached by the sheriff's office in settlement of the shipping agent's unpaid claims. Colt's efforts late in June to retain the apparatus (not since located) for further experiments for the government opened a disheartening decade-long correspondence with the Treasury Department, which was unsatisfied with the inventor's undocumented accounting for requisitions totaling $21,050.62 issued to his account for his Submarine Battery development and experiments. See Sturgis and Clearman to Colt, 23 June 1844; Colt to Charles B. Penrose, Solicitor of the Treasury Department, 24 June 1844, retained copy; William Barrett, U.S. Attorney's Office, New York, to Colt, 29 June and 8 July 1844; A.O. Dayton, Fourth Auditor's Office, Treasury Department, to Colt, 9 December 1844, all in Colt Papers, box 6. See also J.M. Brodhead, Second Comptroller, Treasury Department, to F.B. Streeter, Solicitor of the Treasury Department, 30 November 1854, with attached earlier documents, in Treasury Department, Letters Received from the Second Comptroller, 1821–1894, National Archives, Record Group 206, P.I. 171, Entry 23.

206 EDWARDS, *Colt's Revolver*, pages 277–284 [note 21]; J. LEANDER BISHOP, *A History of American Manufactures from 1608 to 1860...*, 3rd edition, 3 volumes (New York: Johnson Reprint Corp., 1967), volume 3, pages 407–412; VICTOR S. CLARK, *History of Manufactures in the United States, 1607–1860*, revised edition, 3 volumes (Washington: Carnegie Institution, 1929), volume 2, pages 7, 20–21, 87; JOHN W. OLIVER, *History of American Technology* (New York: Ronald Press, 1956), pages 169–170, 263, 279.

207 Colt foresaw few economies for the government if it purchased large quantities of his mining apparatus, as is evident in undated estimates for his "Triangular Submarine Battery" and his "Reflected Submarine Battery," Colt Papers, box 6. EDWARDS, *Colt's Revolver*, pages 211–247 [note 21].

208 WILLIAM LAIRD CLOWES and others, *The Royal Navy: A History from the Earliest Times to the Present*, 7 volumes (London: Sampson Low and Marston, 1897–1903), volume 6, pages 482–484. Concerning British experience with Chinese fireboats and underwater obstructions in 1856–58, see ibid., volume 7, pages 99, 118 and 124–125.

209 PERRY, *Infernal Machines*, pages 5–17 [note 100]; WILLIAMS, *Maury*, pages 376–384, 390–393 [note 100].

210 See in particular SECRETARY OF STATE FOR WAR, *Report on Passive Obstructions for the Defence of Harbours and Channels by the Committee on Floating Obstructions and Submarine Machines* (London: Her Majesty's Stationery Office, 1866); VIKTOR ERNST RUDOLPH VON SCHELIHA, *A Treatise on Coast Defence: Based on the Experiences Gained by Officers of the Corps of Engineers of the Army of the Confederate States....* (London: E. Spon, 1868); and HENRY L. ABBOT, *Submarine Mining in the Defense of Harbors and Rivers* (Willets Point, N.Y.: Battalion Press, 1877); HENRY L. ABBOT, *Report on Experiments and Investigations to Develop a System of Submarine Mines for Defending the Harbors of the United States....* (Willets Point, N.Y.: Battalion Press, 1880).

Notes to the Figures

Figure 1. Mezzotint by Edward Fisher after a portrait of Franklin by Mason Chamberlain in 1762. Smithsonian Institution negative no. 46835–J. CARL VAN DOREN, *Benjamin Franklin* (New York: Viking Press, 1938), pages 156–173, 272–288, 535–537; WORTHINGTON CHAUNCY FORD, editor, *Correspondence and Journals of Samuel Blachley Webb, 1772–1779* (New York [Lancaster, Pennsylvania: Wickersham Press], 1893), pages 163n–164n; SAMUEL HAZARD, et al., editor, *Pennsylvania Archives: Selected and Arranged from Original Documents in the Office of the Secretary of the Commonwealth*, 109 volumes in nine series (Philadelphia: Joseph Severns & Co., 1852–1856), first series, volume 4, pages 650–654; I. MINNIS HAYS, editor, *Calendar of the Papers of Benjamin Franklin in the Library of the American Philosophical Society*, 5 volumes (Philadelphia: American Philosophical Society, 1908), volume 2, pages 23, 30, and volume 4, page 304; WILLIAM BELL CLARK and WILLIAM JAMES MORGAN, editors, *Naval Documents of the American Revolution*, multivolume edition (Washington: Government Printing Office, 1964 to date), volume 1, pages 1088–1089.

Figure 2. Smithsonian Institution negative no. 77114. FREDERICK WAGNER, *Submarine Fighter of the American Revolution: The Story of David Bushnell* (New York: Dodd, Mead & Company, 1963), pages 83–89, 128; EVANS M. WOODWARD and JOHN F. HAGEMAN, *History of Burlington and Mercer Counties, New Jersey, with Bibliographical Sketches of Many of Their Pioneers and Prominent Men* (Philadelphia: Everts and Peck, 1883), pages 463–465; I. MINNIS HAYS, editor, *Calendar of the Papers of Benjamin Franklin in the Library of the American Philosophical Society*, 5 volumes (Philadelphia: American Philosophical Society, 1908), volume 1, page 519; JAMES D. MAGEE, *Bordentown, 1682–1932: An Illustrated Story of a Colonial Town* (Bordentown, New Jersey: The Bordentown Register, 1930), pages 30–40; Record Book of the Philadelphia Museum, Charles Willson Peale Papers, The Historical Society of Pennsylvania, Philadelphia.

Figure 3. Smithsonian Institution negative no. 72–2884. HOWARD L. BLACKMORE, *British Military Firearms, 1650–1850* (London: Herbert Jenkins, 1961), page 57.

Figure 4. Portrait by E. D. Turina. Smithsonian Institution negative no. 72–9336. A. V. ÎAROTSKIĬ, *Pavel L'vovich Schilling* (Moscow: Izdatel' stvo Akademii Nauk SSSR, 1963), pages 9–21.

Figure 5. Portrait courtesy of the Institution of Royal Engineers, Chatham, England. H. W. TYLER, "Memoir of General Sir Charles William Pasley, KCB," *Professional Papers of the Corps of Royal Engineers*, new series, volume 12 (1863), pages ix-xv.

Figure 6. Portrait by Samuel Laurence, in KARL WERCK-MEISTER, editor, *Das neunzehnte Jahrhundert in Bildnissen*, 5 vols. (Berlin: Photographische Gesellschaft, 1898–1901), volume 2, plate 199. Smithsonian Institution negative no. 52331. See LATIMER CLARK, "On the late Sir Charles Wheatstone," *Journal of the Society of Telegraph Engineers*, volume 4 (1875), pages 319–334; ROLLO APPLEYARD, *Pioneers of Electrical Communication* (London: Macmillan & Co., 1930), pages 84–106; E.A. MARLAND, *Early Electrical Communication* (London, New York and Toronto: Abelard-Schuman Ltd., 1964), pages 74–82; P.H. KEALY, *General Sir Charles William Pasley, KCB, FRS, DCL, Colonel Commandant R.E., 1780–1861* (London: privately printed, 1930), pages 77–85.

Figure 7. From ROBERT FULTON, *Torpedo Warfare and Submarine Explosions* (Washington: privately printed, 1810). Smithsonian Institution negative no. 77608–1. Reprinted in Senate Document No. 80: "Use of the Torpedo in the Defence of Ports and Harbors," 11th Congress, 2nd Session, in WALTER LOWRIE and WALTER S. FRANKLIN, editors, *American State Papers . . .*, 38 volumes (Washington: Gales and Seaton, 1832–1861), *Naval Affairs*, volume 1 (1834), pages 211–227, plate 1.

Figure 8. Engraving by J.C. Buttre from a photograph by P. Graff. Smithsonian Institution negative no. 57438. WILLIAM B. EDWARDS, *The Story of Colt's Revolver: The Biography of Col. Samuel Colt* (Harrisburg: Stackpole Co., 1953); JACK ROHAN, *Yankee Arms Maker: The Incredible Career of Samuel Colt* (New York: Harper & Brothers, 1953).

Figure 9. Portrait of Robert Hare by Rembrandt Peale, circa 1820–25, in Independence Hall Historical Park, Philadelphia. Smithsonian Institution negative no. 56579. EDWARD FAHS SMITH, *The Life of Robert Hare: An American Chemist, 1781–1858* (Philadelphia: J.B. Lippincott Co., 1917, pages 3–12, 62–67, 325, 371–384.

Figure 10. Smithsonian Institution negative no. 77972. *The American Journal of Science and Arts*, volume 2 (1820), pages 312–318 and plates at end of volume.

Figure 11. Courtesy of the Division of Physical Sciences, The National Museum of History and Technology, Smithsonian Institution. Catalogue no. 316,886. Smithsonian Institution negative no. 71347.

Figure 12. Courtesy of the Division of Physical Sciences, The National Museum of History and Technology, Smithsonian Institution. Catalogue no. 321,530. Smithsonian Institution negative no. 78000–A.

Figure 13. Detail of drawing "no. 3," Samuel Colt Collection, reproduced by permission of the Connecticut State Library Museum, Hartford. Smithsonian Institution negative no. 76759–B.

Figure 14. Portrait by unknown photographer, reproduced by permission of the Werner-von-Siemens Institute, Munich. Smithsonian Institution negative no. 76824. WERNER VON SIEMENS, *Inventor and Entrepreneur: Recollections of Werner von Siemens.* Introduction by Ernst von Siemens. (London and Munich: Percy Lund Humphries & Co. and Prestel Verlag, 1966), pages 11–70 ff; FRIEDRICH VON EHRENKROOK, *Geschichte der Seeminen und Torpedos* (Berlin: E.S. Mittler & Sohn, 1878), pages 20–22.

Figure 15. Drawing "E", Samuel Colt Collection, reproduced by permission of the Connecticut State Library Museum, Hartford. Smithsonian Institution negative no. 76759–J. For a contemporary representation of light reflected from a canted convex mirror, see JOHN FARRAR, *An Experimental Treatise in Optics . . . for the Use of the Students of the University* (Cambridge: [Harvard] University Press, 1826), pages 16–18, plate 1, figure 11.

Figure 16. Drawing "F", Samuel Colt Collection, reproduced by permission of the Connecticut State Library Museum, Hartford. Smithsonian Institution negative no. 76759–D.

Figure 17. Watercolor by William Siebe, reproduced by permission of the Institution of Royal Engineers and the Royal Engineers Museum at Chatham. T.W.J. CONNOLLY, *History of the Royal Sappers and Miners, from the Foundation of the Corps in March 1772 to the Date When Its Designation Was Changed to That of Royal Engineers, in October 1856,* 2 volumes (London: Longman, Brown, Green, Longmans and Roberts, 1857), volume 1, pages 188, 348–353; P.H. KEALY, *General Sir Charles William Pasley KCB, FRS, DCL, Colonel Commandant R.E., 1780–1861* (London: privately printed, 1930), pages 30, 67–85; *Army and Navy Chronicle,* volume 8 (1839), pages 373–375, and volume 10 (1840), page 100.

Figure 18. Portrait of Southard as Secretary of the Navy by A.S. Conrad, courtesy of the Naval History Division, Department of the Navy. Negative no. NH 77358 KN. CHARLES OSCAR PAULLIN, *Paullin's History of Naval Administration, 1775–1911* (Annapolis: United States Naval Institute, 1968), pages 160–164, 179–183; *Niles' Weekly Register,* volume 20 (30 September 1823), pages 33–34; Washington *Daily National Intelligencer,* 28 June 1842, JAMES RUSSELL SOLEY, *Historical Sketch of the United States Naval Academy* (Washington: Government Printing Office, 1876), pages 14–23.

Figure 19. Engraving by J. Haller from a photograph by Leon Levitzky in St. Petersburg, by permission of the Werner-von-Siemens Institute, Munich. Smithsonian Institution negative no. 58088. Many of Jacobi's mine warfare contributions, including use of the mercury switch, are reprinted in A.A. SAMAROV and F.A. PETROV, editors, *Razvitie minnogo oruzhiya v russkom flote: Dokumenty* [The Development of Mine Materiel in the Russian Navy: Documents] (Moscow: Voenno-morskoe izdatel'stvo voenno-morskogo ministerstva soiuza SSSR, 1951). See also H. WILD, "Rede zum Gedächtnis an H.M. Jacobi, gehalten am 29 December 1875 in der feierlichen Sitzung der Akademie der Wissenschaften," *Bulletin de l'Académie Impériale des Sciences de Saint-Petersbourg,* volume 21 (1876), pages 262–268.

Figure 20. Engraving by unknown artist in *The Scientific American,* volume 2, number 16 (9 January 1847), page 126. Smithsonian Institution negative no. 72–2891. See THEODORE FRANCIS JONES, editor, *New York University, 1832–1932* (New York: New York University Press, 1933), pages 43, 57–58, 393–397; THEODORE WINTHROP, *Cecil Dreeme* (New York: Henry Holt, 1876), pages 33–36; WILLIAM B. EDWARDS, *The Story of Colt's Revolver: The Biography of Col. Samuel Colt* (Harrisburg: Stackpole Co., 1953), pages 191–193; EDWARD LIND MORSE, editor, *Samuel F. B. Morse: His Letters and Journals,* 2 volumes (Boston: Houghton Mifflin Co., 1914), volume 2, pages 37–44, 183–184.

Figure 21. Photographic portrait of Morse circa 1845 by unknown photographer. Courtesy of the Division of Graphic Arts, The National Museum of History and Technology, Smithsonian Institution. Smithsonian Institution negative no. 73–1504. EDWARD LIND MORSE, editor, *Samuel F.B. Morse: His Letters and Journals,* 2 volumes (Boston: Houghton Mifflin Co., 1914); CARLETON MABEE, *The American Leonardo: A Life of Samuel F.B. Morse* (New York: Alfred A. Knopf, 1943); New York *Herald,* 19 October 1842; WILLIAM B. EDWARDS, *The Story of Colt's Revolver: The Biography of Col. Samuel Colt* (Harrisburg: Stackpole Co., 1953), pages 178–179, 191–203.

Figure 22. *The Scientific American,* new series, volume 5, number 9 (31 August 1861), pages 129–132; FRANK M. BENNETT, *The Steam Navy of the United States* (Pittsburgh: Warren & Co., 1896), pages 57–60.

Figure 23. Drawing "N," in Samuel Colt Collection, reproduced by permission of the Connecticut State Library Museum, Hartford. Smithsonian Institution negative no. 73–10240. *The Scientific American,* volume 1, number 12 (4 December 1845), page 46.

Figure 24. Photographic portrait of Perry by Matthew Brady, courtesy of the Library of Congress. Smithsonian Institution negative no. 77792. SAMUEL ELIOT MORISON, *"Old Bruin": Commodore Matthew C. Perry, 1794–1858* (Boston: Little, Brown and Co., 1967), pages 26–143; New York *Herald,* 19 October 1842; Diary of Samuel Colt, 4 June 1842, Samuel Colt Papers (manuscripts, Connecticut Historical Society, Hartford), box 6.

Figure 25. Daguerreotype by John Plumbe, Jr., circa 1846, courtesy of the Prints and Photographs Division of the Library of Congress. Negative no. 31707/46805. See *The United States Magazine,* volume 3, pages 288–298; Henry L. Ellsworth to Colt, 15 August 1843, Samuel Colt Papers (manuscripts, Connecticut Historical Society, Hartford), box 6.

Figure 26. Wood engraving from *Harper's Weekly,* 16 March 1861, courtesy of the Prints and Photographs Division of the Library of Congress. Negative no. 31707/2220. WILLIAM B. EDWARDS, *The Story of Colt's Revolver: The Biography of Col. Samuel Colt* (Harrisburg: Stackpole Co., 1953), pages 144–148; STEPHEN V. BENÉT, editor, *A Collection of Annual Reports and Other Important Papers Relating to the Ordnance Department. . .* (Washington: Government Printing Office, 1878), page 422.

Figure 27. Engraving by J. Haller from a photograph by Schmith. Smithsonian Institution negative no. 77817. FRANCIS LEIGH WILLIAMS, *Matthew Fontaine Maury, Scientist of the Sea* (New Brunswick, New Jersey: Rutgers University Press, 1963).

Figure 28. Drawing "G," Samuel Colt Collection, reproduced by permission of the Connecticut State Library Museum, Hartford. Smithsonian Institution negative no. 76759–E.

Figure 29. Drawing "I," Samuel Colt Collection, reproduced by permission of the Connecticut State Library Museum, Hartford. Smithsonian Institution negative no 76759–C.

Figure 30. Photograph of the Colt cable, which was donated to the Connecticut State Library Museum by the Western Union Telegraph Company, reproduced by permission of that museum. Smithsonian Institution negative no. 73–10239. WILLIAM B. EDWARDS, *The Story of Colt's Revolver: The Biography of Col. Samuel Colt* (Harrisburg: Stackpole Co., 1953), pages 172, 177–178, 191–193; J. LEANDER BISHOP, *A History of American Manufactures from 1608 to 1860. . . ,* third edition, 3 volumes (New York: Johnson Reprint Corp., 1967), volume 3, pages 412–413.

Figure 31. Courtesy of the Samuel Colt Papers (manuscripts, Connecticut Historical Society, Hartford), box 6.

Figure 32. Reproduced by permission of Caldwell C. Robinson of Trappe, Maryland. Smithsonian Institution negative no. 72–10934.

Figure 33. Lithograph by Nathaniel Currier, courtesy of the Prints and Photographs Division, Library of Congress. Negative no. 23399/1.

Figure 34. Reproduced by permission of the Samuel Colt Collection, Connecticut State Library Museum, Hartford. Smithsonian Institution negative no. 76759–G.

Figure 35. Portion of drawing "A" reproduced by permission of the Samuel Colt Collection, Connecticut State Library Museum, Hartford. Smithsonian Institution negative no. 76759–K. See WILLIAM B. EDWARDS, *The Story of Colt's Revolver: The Biography of Col. Samuel Colt* (Harrisburg: Stackpole Co., 1953), pages 195–200 and appendix.

Figure 36. Reproduced by permission of Samuel Colt Collection, Connecticut State Library Museum, Hartford. Smithsonian Institution negative no. 76759–I. See also the document "Signals Ship Styx," Samuel Colt Papers (manuscripts, Connecticut Historical Society, Hartford), box 6.

Figure 37. Engraving by W.J. Bennett in 1834, after a painting by G. Cooke, courtesy of the Prints and Photographs Division of the Library of Congress. Negative no. 31707/2737. See also Colt to Secretary of the Navy John Y. Mason, 22 April 1844, retained copy, Samuel Colt Papers (manuscripts, Connecticut Historical Society, Hartford), box 6.

Figure 38. Detail reproduced by permission of Caldwell

C. Robinson of Trappe, Maryland. Smithsonian Institution negative no. 72–10936. ALLEN C. CLARK, *Greenleaf and Law in the Federal City* (Washington: W. F. Roberts Press, 1901), page 246; log of the U.S.S. *Union,* 1844, Record Group 24, National Archives.

Figure 39. Daguerreotype portrait of Joseph Henry about 1842–45 by an unknown photographer. Reproduced by permission of the Chicago Historical Society. Smithsonian Institution negative no. SA12. See Secretary of War William Wilkins to Joseph Henry, 29 April 1844, in *Colt's Submarine Battery,* House Document No. 127, 28th Congress, 2nd Session, pages 2 and 11. See also Morse to Henry, 27 March 1844; William Hamilton to Henry, 1 April 1844; Henry to Alexander Dallas Bache, 16 April 1844, retained copy, all in Joseph Henry Papers (manuscripts, Smithsonian Institution Archives); THOMAS COULSON, *Joseph Henry: His Life and His Work* (Princeton: Princeton University Press, 1950), pages 12–31, 38–43, 46–168; NATHAN REINGOLD, editor, *The Papers of Joseph Henry,* multivolume edition (Washington: Smithsonian Institution Press, 1973 to date) volume 1, pages 3, 54–57, 60–61, 77–92, 132–133, 201, 217, 316–320, 433–441, 456–459.

Figure 40. Portrait by Robert W. Weir, courtesy of the West Point Museum. GEORGE W. CULLUM, *Biographical Register of the Officers and Graduates of the United States Military Academy,* 3rd edition, 2 volumes (Boston: Houghton, Mifflin, Co., 1891), pages 63–67; WILLIAM J. RHEES, editor, *The Smithsonian Institution: Documents Relative to its Origin and History, 1835-1899,* 2 volumes (Washington: Smithsonian Institution, 1901), page 438.

Figure 41. The annotations on this drawing ("No. 3") and the elfin operative appear to have been added later by Charles Brinckerhoff Richards, who served as engineering superintendent of Colt's Armory during the entrepreneur's last years. From the Samuel Colt Collection, reproduced by permission of the Connecticut State Library Museum, Hartford. Smithsonian Institution negative no. 76759–B. N.G. OSBORN, *Men of Mark of Connecticut: Ideals of American Life Told in Biographies and Autobiographies of Eminent Living Americans,* 5 volumes (Hartford: N.R. Goodspeed Co., 1906–1910), volume 1, pages 309–310.

Figure 42. Portion of Drawing "A," Samuel Colt Collection, reproduced by permission of the Connecticut State Library Museum, Hartford. Smithsonian Institution negative no. 76759–F.

Figure 43. Adjacent portion of Drawing "A," Samuel Colt Collection, reproduced by permission of the Connecticut State Library Museum, Hartford. Smithsonian Institution negative no. 76759–H.

Index

☆U.S. GOVERNMENT PRINTING OFFICE: 1974 O—531–605